Statistics for construction students

J A Bland B.Sc., Ph.D., AFIMA

Trent Polytechnic
Nottingham

Construction Press
London and New York

General Editor: Colin Bassett BSc, FCIOB, FFB

Construction Press
an imprint of:

Longman Group Limited
Longman House, Burnt Mill, Harlow
Essex CM20 2JE, England
Associated companies throughout the world

Published in the United States of America
by Longman Inc., New York

First published 1985

British Library Cataloguing in Publication Data
Bland, J.A.
   Statistics for construction students.
   1. Building − Statistical methods
   I. Title
   519.5′024624   TH153

ISBN 0-86095-043-3

Library of Congress Cataloging in Publication Data
Bland, J.A., 1951−
   Statistics for construction students.

   Bibliography: p.
   Includes index.
   1. Engineering—Statistical methods.   2. Probabilities.
   I. Title.
   TA340.B58 1985   624′028   84—19946
   ISBN 0—86095—043—3

Printed in Great Britain by
The Bath Press, Avon

Contents

Preface

Statistics for Construction Students is written for students of building in colleges, polytechnics and universities. It may also be of use to students of civil engineering and surveying.

The aims of this book are:

(a) To explain statistical ideas and methods;
(b) To show construction applications of statistics.

With regard to the first aim, this book concentrates on probability distributions and so is not intended to be a complete and definitive work on statistics.

Chapter 1, which gives only brief coverage of descriptive statistics, serves to introduce (in the book) terms such as mean and standard deviation, sample and population. Chapter 2, as the title states, is merely an introduction to probability and goes to no greater depth than is required for subsequent chapters. The book proper, in terms of probability distributions, commences with Chapter 3.

To achieve the second aim the statistical backgrounds of topics unique to construction (e.g. the compliance criteria, limit state design) are presented and explained. The use of these topics to integrate statistics and construction is a feature of this book. Furthermore, the overall content (i.e. explanations, worked examples, exercises) has a construction bias.

It is expected that this book will be of use to construction students studying for the following qualifications; HND(BTEC), B.Sc., and CIOB parts I and II. Although statistics is a component of construction courses it is recognized that construction students are not 'main-stream' mathematicians; the mathematical level of this book is no higher than that required of construction students studying for the above qualifications.

In conclusion I should like to thank the following people; Mrs J. Frampton, for the excellent typing of the manuscript; my wife Christine, to whom this book is dedicated, for her support and encouragement throughout the preparation stages; our daughter Victoria, who came along during the writing of Chapter 8 (a small sample?), for not slowing the preparation process any more than she could help.

J A Bland
Trent Polytechnic
Nottingham

Acknowledgements

The author wishes to thank the following for permission to reproduce copyright material:

(a) The McGraw-Hill Book Company (UK) Limited, for the normal distribution table (Table A.1).

(b) John Wiley and Sons Ltd, for the t-distribution table and χ^2-distribution table (Table A.2 and Table A.3, respectively).

(c) The British Standards Institution.

Extracts from British Standards are reproduced by permission of the British Standards Institution, 2 Park Street, London, W1A 2BS, from whom complete copies of the standards can be obtained.

Presentation of data

1.1 Introduction

Many situations occur in construction which involve a large amount of data (e.g. compressive strength values obtained from test cubes of concrete, the number of various building components used in a construction project). Often each individual item of data is unimportant by itself and must be considered in relation to the other data. In other words, when large amounts of data are considered their *relative* values are sometimes more important than their *absolute* values.

In order to investigate and analyse a large amount of data so that values, or groups of values, can be compared, statistical methods in the form of pictures and graphs are used. Data presented in this manner enables comparisons to be made 'at a glance' and information to be readily obtained.

1.2 Pictorial presentation of data

A large amount of data which has not been organized numerically is called **raw data**. As an example consider the numbers of houses built by a local authority on 100 housing schemes over a five-year period. The raw data is displayed in Table 1.1.

Table 1.1 Raw data; houses built during the period 1975−79, year of completion given in brackets

100(75)	38(75)	44(76)	35(76)	85(77)	78(77)	76(78)	280(78)	56(79)	184(79)
152(75)	86(75)	82(76)	100(76)	143(77)	121(77)	156(78)	122(78)	360(79)	63(79)
68(75)	73(75)	20(76)	64(77)	155(77)	87(77)	29(78)	78(78)	235(79)	45(79)
104(75)	62(75)	84(76)	156(77)	82(77)	61(77)	188(78)	46(78)	36(79)	226(79)
50(75)	100(75)	96(76)	94(77)	262(77)	37(77)	76(78)	56(78)	99(79)	169(79)
45(75)	64(75)	89(76)	21(77)	74(77)	63(77)	154(78)	98(78)	310(79)	80(79)
84(75)	36(75)	32(76)	91(77)	23(77)	81(77)	40(78)	74(79)	58(79)	98(79)
122(75)	55(75)	68(76)	50(77)	158(77)	19(77)	272(78)	28(79)	127(79)	30(79)
168(75)	28(75)	20(76)	172(77)	140(77)	100(77)	50(78)	127(79)	72(79)	36(79)
65(75)	35(76)	45(76)	28(77)	55(77)	93(78)	36(78)	68(79)	385(79)	34(79)

In order to make sense of the raw data it must be organized into groups. The grouping or **tabulation** of the raw data depends on what comparisons are required (or desirable). For instance, with the housing schemes, if the number of houses built per year is being investigated, then the raw data can be tabulated on a yearly basis, as shown in Table 1.2.

Table 1.2

Year	Number of houses built
1975	1500
1976	750
1977	2500
1978	1850
1979	3000

Several methods of presenting the tabulated data pictorially are now given. The motivation for this pictorial presentation of data is that columns of numbers can be uninspiring and do not readily indicate trends 'at a glance'.

(a) Pie diagrams

A **pie diagram** represents groups of data (here the number of houses in a given year) as a sector of a circle. The angle of the sector (and hence the area) for each group being in proportion to the value of the group.

The total number of houses built in the five-year period is

N = 1500 + 750 + 2500 + 1850 + 3000
    = 9600 houses

Hence 9600 represents 360° and the sector angles can be calculated as shown in Table 1.3.

Using the data in Table 1.3 a pie diagram can be constructed and is shown in Fig. 1.1.

Table 1.3 Calculation of sector angles

Year	Number of houses, n	Fraction of total, $\dfrac{n}{N}$	Sector angle $\left(\dfrac{n}{N}\right)360°$
1975	1500	0.156	56°
1976	750	0.078	28°
1977	2500	0.260	94°
1978	1850	0.193	69°
1979	3000	0.313	113°

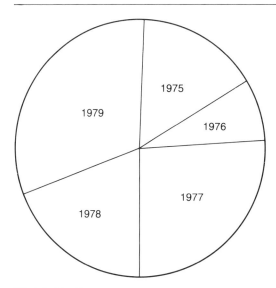

Fig 1.1 Pie diagram

A pie diagram is used to compare groups and not to determine their values. For instance, by comparing sector areas, the pie diagram in Fig. 1.1 indicates that more houses were built in 1977 than the year before but it does not reveal how many houses were built in those years.

(b) Ideographs

An **ideograph** represents each group of data as a number of suitable pictures (ideographs are sometimes called **pictograms**). The pictures are all of the same size and denote a fixed value, as shown in Fig. 1.2.

Ideographs are used to compare groups of data by observing the difference in the number of pictures representing each group. They can also give the value of the group since each picture denotes a known fixed value. However, precision is lost when a proportion of a picture is encountered.

(c) Picturegrams

Unlike ideographs, **picturegrams** represent each group of data as a single picture. The picture for each group is of the same object but its size is in proportion to the value of the group. A picturegram for the local authority housing schemes is shown in Fig. 1.3.

A picturegram is used to compare groups by observing the difference in the sizes of associated pictures. The picturegram in Fig. 1.3 can also be used to indicate the value of each group since the reference base length denotes 1000 houses. However, if no key were given then the picturegram could not indicate the group values and even comparison becomes difficult because there would be confusion as to whether lengths or areas were being compared.

3

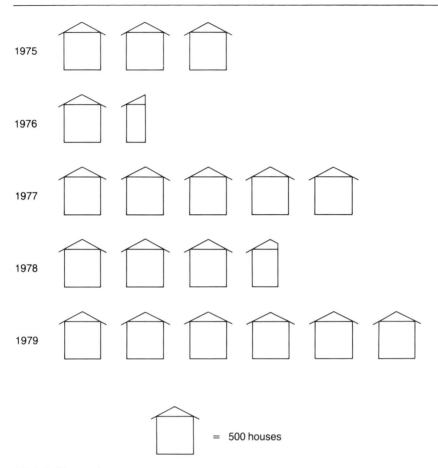

Fig 1.2 Ideograph

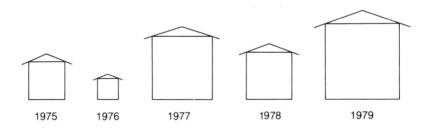

Base length ├────┤ = 1000 houses

Fig 1.3 Picturegram

(d) Bar charts

Bar charts represent the value of each group of data as a length of bar, as shown in Fig. 1.4.

A bar chart is one of the most useful ways of presenting data since groups are easily compared by observing the differences in bar heights and, with reference to the given vertical scale, their values can be determined.

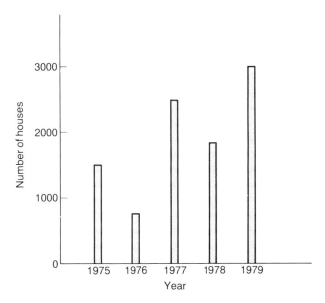

Fig 1.4 Bar chart

1.3   Graphical presentation of data

In the previous section the presentation of data concentrated mostly on comparison; in this section numerical values will be equally important.

If, for example, 100 pieces of timber are delivered to a building site and their lengths are measured and recorded (to the nearest centimetre), then the results can be summarized in a **frequency distribution** (or **frequency table**) as shown in Table 1.4.

Table 1.4 Frequency distribution

Length (cm)	Number of pieces of timber
60–62	5
63–65	18
66–68	42
69–71	29
72–74	6

5

The first column of Table 1.4 contains the length **classes** and the second column gives the **class frequencies** (i.e. the number of pieces of timber in each class).

With reference to Table 1.4, the interval denoted by 60−62 is called the **class interval**; 60 and 62 being the **class limits**. Now since the timber lengths are recorded to the nearest centimetre the class frequency includes all measurements between exactly 59.5 cm and just less than 62.5 cm (a piece of timber with length exactly 62.5 cm would be included in the class interval 63−65). Hence 59.5 and 62.5 are called the **class boundaries** (see Fig. 1.5) and the **class width** is 62.5−59.5 = 3 cm. The mid-point between the boundaries is called the **class mid-point** and is given by (59.5 + 62.5)/2 = 61 cm.

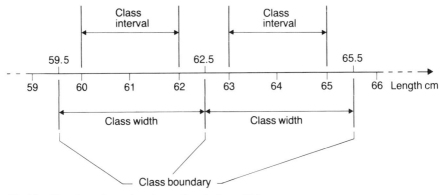

Fig 1.5 Class boundary, class interval and class width

The data in the frequency distribution can be presented graphically in the following ways.

(a) Histogram and frequency polygon

A **histogram** for the data in Table 1.4 is shown in Fig. 1.6. It comprises vertical columns drawn side by side on a horizontal axis denoting length. The columns meet the horizontal axis at the class boundaries and their heights denote class frequency as measured by the vertical scale.

A **frequency polygon** corresponding to Table 1.4 is shown by the broken lines in Fig. 1.6; the mid-points of the tops of the columns are connected by straight lines. By considering class intervals 57−59 and 75−77 with zero frequency the frequency polygon is 'anchored' to the base at class mid-points 58 cm and 76 cm, respectively (this could not be achieved if the class intervals in Table 1.4 were unequal).

(b) Relative frequency histogram

The **relative frequency** of a class is the frequency of the class divided by the total frequency of all classes (and is sometimes expressed as a percentage). For example, the relative frequency of the first class in Table 1.4 is 5/100 = 0.05 (or 5%). Clearly the sum of all relative frequencies is 1 (or 100%).

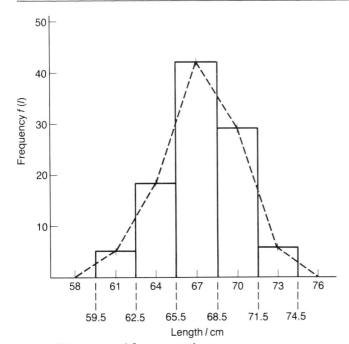

Fig 1.6   Histogram and frequency polygon

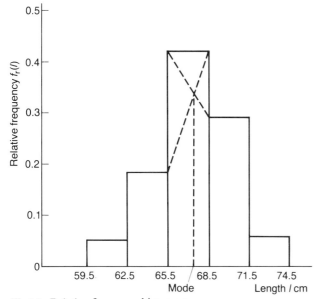

Fig 1.7   Relative frequency histogram

A **relative frequency histogram** can be obtained from the histogram in Fig. 1.6 by simply changing the vertical scale from frequency, $f(l)$, to relative frequency, $f_r(l)$, keeping exactly the same diagram; see Fig. 1.7.

(c) Cumulative frequency curve

The total frequency of all values less than the upper class boundary of a given class interval is called the **'less than' cumulative frequency**. For example, the 'less than' cumulative frequency for the class interval 66−68 in Table 1.4 is 5 + 18 + 42 = 65 (i.e. 65 pieces of timber have length less than 68.5 cm). Table 1.5 gives the 'less than' cumulative frequencies for the classes in Table 1.4.

A graph of the cumulative frequency less than an upper class boundary plotted against the upper class boundary is called a **'less than' cumulative frequency curve** (or **'less than' ogive**). The 'less than' cumulative frequency curve for the data in Table 1.4 and Table 1.5 is shown in Fig. 1.8.

Although less usual, an 'or more' cumulative frequency curve (or 'or more' ogive) can be obtained by plotting the cumulative frequency equal to or more than a lower class boundary against the lower class boundary.

Table 1.5 Cumulative frequency
distribution

Length (cm)	Cumulative frequency
less than 59.5	0
less than 62.5	5
less than 65.5	23
less than 68.5	65
less than 71.5	94
less than 74.5	100

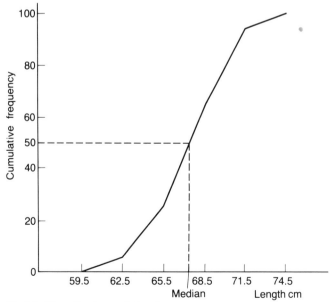

Fig 1.8 'Less than' cumulative frequency curve

1.4   Grading of aggregates

The term 'aggregates' is used to describe the gravels, crushed stones and other materials which are mixed with cement and water to make concrete.

Aggregates usually constitute between 50% and 80% of the volume of concrete and so may greatly influence properties such as strength and shrinkage. Hence the selection of suitable aggregates (with particular attention given to particle size) is important in concrete production.

The proportions of the difference sizes of particles that constitute an aggregate are found by sieving and are known as the *grading* of the aggregate.

As specified in BS 410 (1976) the aperture sizes of the test sieves used in the grading of aggregates are 50.0, 37.5, 20.0, 14.0, 10.0, 5.0 mm made with perforated plate and 2.36, 1.18 mm, 600, 300, 150 μm made with woven wire.

In BS 882 (1983) distinction is made between aggregates;

(a)   coarse aggregate is mainly retained on a 5.0 mm BS 410 test sieve
(b)   fine aggregate mainly passes a 5.0 mm BS 410 test sieve
(c)   all-in aggregate is a mixture of fine and coarse aggregate.

Also, BS 882 specifies grading limits for the above classes of aggregate; those for fine aggregate are given in Table 1.6.

As shown in Table 1.6 a wide range of gradings of fine aggregate is acceptable for concrete (C, M and F indicate a progressively finer material).

Table 1.6   Grading limits for fine aggregate; after BS 882

| | *Percentage by mass passing BS sieve* | | | |
| | | *Additional limits for grading* | | |
Sieve size	Overall limits	C	M	F
10.00 mm	100	—	—	—
5.00 mm	89–100	—	—	—
2.36 mm	60–100	60–100	65–100	80–100
1.18 mm	30–100	30–90	45–100	70–100
600 μm	15–100	15–54	25–80	55–100
300 μm	5–70	5–40	5–48	5–70
150 μm	0–15	—	—	—

The data in Table 1.6 becomes more informative when the grading limits are presented graphically as 'percentage passing' cumulative frequency curves. The overall grading limits for fine aggregate are shown in broken line in Fig. 1.9 together with grade C additional limits in continuous line.

Similar cumulative frequency curves can be constructed for the grading limits of coarse and all-in aggregate.

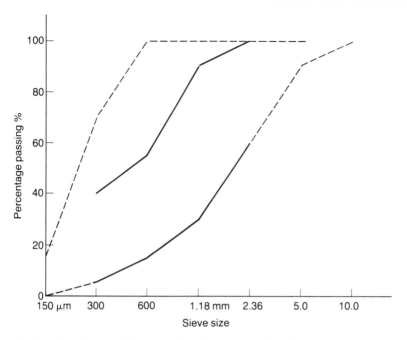

Fig 1.9 Overall and additional grading limits for grade C fine aggregate

1.5 Averages and dispersion

An **average** is a general term used to denote a value which is typical or representative of a set of data. There are several types of average; the **mean** (i.e. arithmetic mean), the **median** and the **mode**.

The degree to which numerical data tend to spread about an average value is called the **dispersion** of the data, the most common measures of dispersion being the **range** and the **standard deviation**.

The statistical methods used to determine an average and dispersion of a set of data differ according to whether the data is considered as individual values or as tabulated data in a frequency distribution, that is, **ungrouped** or **grouped data**, respectively.

(a) Ungrouped data

For a set of n values x_1, x_2, ..., x_n the mean, range and standard deviation are defined mathematically as

$$\text{mean} = \frac{\sum_{i=1}^{n} x_i}{n}$$

$$\text{range} = \max \{x_i\} - \min \{x_i\}$$

10

$$\text{standard deviation} = \sqrt{\left[\frac{\sum_{i=1}^{n}(x_i - \text{mean})^2}{n}\right]}$$

The mode of a set of data is that individual value which occurs with the greatest frequency, i.e. the most common value. Some data may possess more than one mode, or none at all.

The median is the middle value (or mean of the middle values if n is even) when the data is arranged in order of magnitude.

Example 1.1

A building subcontractor pays his eight employees the weekly wages (in pounds) as shown in Table 1.7. Determine the mean, mode and median wage, also the wage range and standard deviation.

Table 1.7 Wages of employees

Employee	1	2	3	4	5	6	7	8
Wage, £W	100	60	70	100	60	100	130	80

$$\text{mean} = \frac{\sum_{i=1}^{8} W_i}{8} = \frac{700}{8} = £87.5$$

mode = most common wage = £100

Rearranging the wages into ascending order gives

60, 60, 70, 80, 100, 100, 100, 130

thus

$$\text{median} = \frac{80 + 100}{2} = £90$$

range = $130 - 60 = £70$

Also

$$\text{standard deviation} = \sqrt{\left[\frac{\sum_{i=1}^{8}(W_i - 87.5)^2}{8}\right]}$$

$$= £22.78$$

(b) Grouped data

To determine the mean and standard deviation of grouped data (i.e. data in a frequency distribution) the **coding method** can be used. This is demonstrated in Table 1.8 for the frequency distribution in Table 1.4.

Table 1.8 Coding method

Class mid-point	u	Frequency f	fu	fu^2
61	−2	5	−10	20
64	−1	18	−18	18
67 (A)	0	42	0	0
70	1	29	29	29
73	2	6	12	24
Sums		100	13	91

In Table 1.8 the first and third columns are the class mid-points and frequencies, respectively, of each class in Table 1.4. In the second column a zero is placed in the same row as the largest frequency (a tie is broken arbitrarily) and the associated class mid-point is labelled A. So here $A = 67$ and all other values of u are calculated from $u = (m - A)/c$, where m and c denote class mid-point and class width respectively. Columns four and five are constructed using the data in columns two and three. The mean and standard deviation are then given by

$$\text{mean} = A + c \left(\frac{\Sigma fu}{n} \right)$$

$$= 67 + 3 \times \frac{13}{100}$$

$$= 67.39 \text{ cm}$$

$$\text{standard deviation} = c \sqrt{\left[\frac{\Sigma fu^2}{n} - \left(\frac{\Sigma fu}{n} \right)^2 \right]}$$

$$= 3 \times \sqrt{\left[\frac{91}{100} - \left(\frac{13}{100} \right)^2 \right]}$$

$$= 2.84 \text{ cm}.$$

It should be recognized that for grouped data the values obtained for the mean and standard deviation are approximate. This is because the value of each member in a class is taken to be the class mid-point, which may not be the case. Accuracy can be improved by using smaller class intervals but this increases the number of classes and hence the amount of computation.

A value for the mode can be obtained graphically from the relative frequency histogram as shown in Fig. 1.7 (or from the histogram in Fig. 1.6). The mode is 67.45 cm.

The median can be obtained graphically from the cumulative frequency curve in Fig. 1.8 by noting the length value corresponding to the cumulative frequency $n/2 = 100/2 = 50$. Hence the median is 67.43 cm.

1.6 Population and sample

The complete or entire set of values of interest in any particular circumstance is called the **population** of values. The number of values comprising the population is the **population size** and this can be finite or infinite.

For a population of size n_p $(x_1, x_2, ..., x_{n_p})$ the mean and standard deviation are denoted by μ and σ, respectively, where

$$\mu = \frac{\sum_{i=1}^{n_p} x_i}{n_p} \qquad [1.1]$$

and

$$\sigma = \sqrt{\left[\frac{\sum_{i=1}^{n_p} (x_i - \mu)^2}{n_p} \right]} \qquad [1.2]$$

However, if instead of considering all the values in a population a certain proportion only is considered, then the set of values comprising the proportion of the population is called a **sample** and the number of values in the sample is the **sample size**.

The mean and standard deviation of a sample of size n are denoted by $\bar{x}$ and s, respectively, where

$$\bar{x} = \frac{\sum_{i=1}^{n} x_i}{n} \qquad [1.3]$$

and

$$s = \sqrt{\left[\frac{\sum_{i=1}^{n} (x_i - \bar{x})^2}{n} \right]} \qquad [1.4]$$

It is important to note that equations [1.3] and [1.4] apply when the mean and standard deviation of *sample values only* are required. Usually with very large (or infinite) populations the population mean and standard deviation are impractical (or impossible) to obtain. In these circumstances the mean and standard deviation of a sample taken from the population can be used to *estimate* the unknown values of μ and σ. Sample estimates of the population mean and standard deviation are denoted by $\hat{\mu}$ and $\hat{\sigma}$, respectively (the circumflex denotes an estimate), and are given by

$$\hat{\mu} = \bar{x} = \frac{\sum_{i=1}^{n} x_i}{n} \qquad\qquad [1.5]$$

and

$$\hat{\sigma} = s \sqrt{\left(\frac{n}{n-1}\right)}$$

that is,

$$\hat{\sigma} = \sqrt{\left[\frac{\sum_{i=1}^{n}(x_i - \bar{x})^2}{n-1}\right]} \qquad\qquad [1.6]$$

In some texts s is written instead of $\hat{\sigma}$ in equation [1.6] thereby introducing a potential source of confusion as to whether the denominator in the equation for the sample standard deviation is n or $n-1$. Although the values of s and $\hat{\sigma}$ (given by equations [1.4] and [1.6], respectively) converge to each other as n increases, there still remains a distinction in their theoretical backgrounds.

Example 1.2

Ten concrete cubes from a mix had the following compressive strengths (in N/mm^2)

25.0, 24.5, 32.5, 33.2, 35.1
30.1, 29.6, 34.0, 30.3, 31.0

Find the mean compressive strength and standard deviation of the mix.
Here the population comprises all concrete in the mix. Estimates of the population mean and standard deviation are given by equations [1.5] and [1.6], respectively:

$$\hat{\mu} = \frac{305.3}{10} = 30.53 \text{ N/mm}^2$$

$$\hat{\sigma} = \sqrt{\frac{\sum_{i=1}^{10}(x_i - 30.53)^2}{9}} = 3.53 \text{ N/mm}^2$$

In contrast, the standard deviation of the given ten compressive strengths is, by equation [1.4],

$$s = \sqrt{\frac{\sum_{i=1}^{10}(x_i - 30.53)^2}{10}} = 3.35 \text{ N/mm}^2$$

Exercises

1. The number of people employed by a certain building company on 1 May each year during the period 1967–71 was 400, 500, 375, 450 and 600 respectively. Present this data as a pie diagram, ideograph, picturegram and bar chart.

2. Use Table 1.6 to construct the overall and additional grading limits for M and F grade fine aggregate.

3. Table 1.9 gives the times taken by bricklaying gangs to erect the brickwork from the damp course level to the underside of the first floor joists for 50 detached houses.

Table 1.9

Time hours	Number of houses
240–249	1
250–259	1
260–269	7
270–279	10
280–289	16
290–299	11
300–309	2
310–319	2

Calculate the mean time taken and the standard deviation of the distribution.

[282.5 hours, 14 hours]

4. Construct a histogram and a cumulative frequency curve for the frequency distribution given in Table 1.9. Hence find the mode and median times.

[284.95 hours, 283.25 hours]

5. The number of hours worked by the 10 employees of a small building firm during a certain week were

45, 46, 43, 47, 43, 44, 42, 46, 42, 43

Calculate the median, mode, mean and standard deviation of the hours worked by the employees.

[43.5 hours, 43 hours, 44.1 hours, 1.7 hours]

6. Concrete cubes from an on-site mix were tested for compressive strength and gave the following results.

Table 1.10

Compressive strength N/mm^2	Number of cubes
25–27	1
28–30	6
31–33	10
34–36	8
37–39	4
40–42	1

Find estimates for the mean compressive strength and standard deviation of the mix.

[33.1 N/mm^2, 3.48 N/mm^2]

Chapter 2

Introduction to probability

2.1   Introduction

In Chapter 1 it was shown how data can be organized and presented in both pictorial and graphical form. This presentation of data (mainly for comparison purposes) is an important aspect of statistics, but a more mathematical approach requires knowledge of probability.

Probability is in fact central to the mathematical study of statistics, so before continuing further with statistics the fundamentals of probability are now explained.

2.2   Definitions

(a)   Probability

Suppose that an event E can occur in m ways out of a total of n possible (equally likely) ways. Then the **probability** of occurrence of the event (called the **probability of success**) is defined as

$$p = P(E) = \frac{m}{n}$$

Hence probability can be regarded as relative frequency i.e. the proportion of the total number of ways that an event occurs.

Since the minimum and maximum values of m are 0 and n, respectively, the minimum and maximum values of p are 0 and 1, respectively. Thus the probability of success can take any value in the interval $0 \leqslant p \leqslant 1$. When $p = 0$ the event cannot occur ($m = 0$) and when $p = 1$ the event must occur ($m = n$).

The probability of non-occurrence of an event E (called the **probability of failure**) is denoted by

$$q = P(\bar{E}) = \frac{n-m}{n}$$

Since $(n-m)/n = 1 - m/n$ it follows that $q = 1 - p$. Hence $p + q = 1$, or $P(E) + P(\bar{E}) = 1$, so that the total probability is unity.

Many situations in which probability is used involve the selection of an item (or items) from a group. Now in order that probability theory can be adequately applied to a particular situation the group items must be such that each is equally likely to be selected, that is, there is no bias to the choice of a particular item. In other words items should be chosen **at random**.

Example 2.1

Each member of the labour force of a construction firm is timed (to the nearest minute) to perform a certain operation. The results are shown in Table 2.1. Supposing that one of the labour force is chosen at random to perform the operation again (under the same conditions as before), find the probability that the chosen member of the labour force

(a) takes between 10 and 14 minutes
(b) does not take more than 19 minutes.

Table 2.1 Frequency distribution
of operation times

Time taken (min)	Number of men
0–9	2
10–14	6
15–19	9
20+	3

Let E_1 = operation performed in 0–9 min
E_2 = operation performed in 10–14 min
E_3 = operation performed in 15–19 min
E_4 = operation performed in 20+   min

(a) The probability that between 10 and 14 minutes are taken to perform the operation is

$$P(E_2) = \frac{\text{number in labour force that take 10–14 min}}{\text{total labour force}}$$

$$= \frac{6}{20} = 0.3$$

(b) To take 'not more than 19 minutes' to perform the operation is equivalent to taking 'not 20 minutes or more', i.e. $P(\bar{E}_4)$ is required.

Now $P(E_4) + P(\bar{E}_4) = 1$
so $P(\bar{E}_4) = 1 - P(E_4)$

$$= 1 - \tfrac{3}{20}$$
$$= 0.85$$

(b) Independent and dependent events

When the occurrence of one event does not affect the probability of the occurrence of another event then the events are called **independent**. For example, with reference to Example 2.1, for a person chosen at random from the labour force

$$P(E_1) = \tfrac{2}{20} \quad, \quad P(E_2) = \tfrac{6}{20}$$
$$P(E_3) = \tfrac{9}{20} \quad, \quad P(E_4) = \tfrac{3}{20}$$

[2.1]

If this person is still considered a member of the labour force (in terms of probability, a process called '**with replacement**') then when another person is chosen (which could be the first person again) the probabilities remain unchanged.

Alternatively, when the probability of occurrence of one event does affect the probability of another event occurring, then the events are called **dependent**. Again, for a person chosen at random from the labour force in Example 2.1, the probabilities are as given in equations [2.1]. However, if this person took, for example, between 0 and 9 minutes to complete the operation and now leaves the labour force (the process is then said to be **without replacement**), then when another person is chosen the probabilities are

$$P(E_1) = \tfrac{1}{19} \quad, \quad P(E_2) = \tfrac{6}{19}$$
$$P(E_3) = \tfrac{9}{19} \quad, \quad P(E_4) = \tfrac{3}{19}$$

(c) Mutually exclusive events

Two or more events are called **mutually exclusive** if the occurrence of one of them excludes the occurrence of the others, i.e. when not more than one of these events can happen at the same time. For instance, in Example 2.1, events E_1, E_2, E_3 and E_4 are all mutually exclusive since for a person chosen at random from the labour force only one of the events will occur.

2.3   Laws of probability

(a) The addition law

For two mutually exclusive events, E_1 and E_2, the probability of either the first event or the second event occurring is given by

$$P(E_1 \text{ or } E_2) = P(E_1) + P(E_2)$$

This **addition law** of probabilities can be generalized for n mutually exclusive events

$$P(E_1 \text{ or } E_2 \text{ or } ... \text{ or } E_n)$$
$$= P(E_1) + P(E_2) + ... + P(E_n)$$

(b) The multiplication law

For both dependent and independent events the probability of both event E_1 and event

E_2 occurring is given by

$$P(E_1 \text{ and } E_2) = P(E_1)P(E_2)$$

where, for dependent events, $P(E_2)$ denotes the probability of occurrence of E_2 given that E_1 has occurred; sometimes written as $P(E_2 \mid E_1)$.

For n events the **multiplication law** can be generalized to

$$P(E_1 \text{ and } E_2 \text{ and } \dots E_n)$$
$$= P(E_1)P(E_2) \dots P(E_n)$$

Again, for dependent events, $P(E_i)$, $i = 2, 3, \dots, n$, denotes the probability of occurrence of E_i given that $E_{i-1}, E_{i-2}, \dots, E_1$ have all occurred, i.e. $P(E_i \mid E_{i-1}, E_{i-2}, \dots, E_1)$.

Example 2.2

A plant hire firm has a fleet of bulldozers; 8 are five years old, 5 are three years old and 2 are one year old.

(a) Given that one is hired (at random) by a contractor, find the probability that it is
   (i) more than two years old.
   (ii) not three years old.
(b) A week later the same contractor hires a second bulldozer; find the probability that
   (i) both bulldozers are one year old
   (ii) the first is five years old and the second is three years old.

Let E_1 = one-year old bulldozer hired
   E_2 = three-year old bulldozer hired
   E_3 = five-year old bulldozer hired

(a) The probabilities of hiring a bulldozer are

$$P(E_1) = \tfrac{2}{15}, \qquad P(E_2) = \tfrac{5}{15} = \tfrac{1}{3} \quad \text{and} \quad P(E_3) = \tfrac{8}{15}$$

   (i) For a bulldozer to be more than two years old it must be either three or five years old; that is,

$$P(E_2 \text{ or } E_3) = P(E_2) + P(E_3)$$
$$= \tfrac{1}{3} + \tfrac{8}{15} = \tfrac{13}{15}$$

   (ii) If a bulldozer is not three years old it is either one or five years old; that is,

$$P(E_1 \text{ or } E_3) = P(E_1) + P(E_3)$$
$$= \tfrac{2}{15} + \tfrac{8}{15} = \tfrac{2}{3}$$

   This result can also be obtained from $P(\bar{E}_2) = 1 - P(E_2)$.

(b) The second bulldozer is hired without replacement of the first and so the fleet now comprises 14 bulldozers; the hiring of the first and second bulldozers are dependent events.

(i) For the first bulldozer $P(E_1) = \frac{2}{15}$

For the second bulldozer $P(E_1) = P(E_1 \mid E_1) = \frac{1}{14}$ so
$P(E_1 \text{ and } E_1) = P(E_1)P(E_1 \mid E_1)$
$$= \frac{2}{15} \times \frac{1}{14}$$
$$= \frac{1}{105}$$

(ii) For the first bulldozer $P(E_3) = \frac{8}{15}$

For the second bulldozer $P(E_2) = P(E_2 \mid E_3) = \frac{5}{14}$
so $P(E_3 \text{ and } E_2) = P(E_3)P(E_2 \mid E_3)$
$$= \frac{8}{15} \times \frac{5}{14}$$
$$= \frac{4}{21}$$

2.4 Probability distributions

If a variable x can assume a finite number of values; x_1, x_2, ..., x_n, so that the respective probabilities of occurrence $P(x_1)$, $P(x_2)$, ..., $P(x_n)$ are such that

$$\sum_{i=1}^{n} P(x_i) = 1$$

then the $P(x_i)$, $i = 1, 2, ..., n$, represent a **discrete probability distribution** for the variable x (which is called a **discrete random variable**) and can be presented graphically as shown in the example in Fig. 2.1 for $n = 5$. Notice that Fig. 2.1 can also be thought of as a relative frequency histogram since, by Section 2.2(a), probability can be regarded as relative frequency.

Now if instead of taking a finite number of values the variable x can assume an infinite and continuous number of values in, for example, the interval $x_1 < x < x_n$, then it is called a **continuous random variable** and has a **continuous probability distribution** (see Fig. 2.2) such that

$$\int_{x_1}^{x_n} P(x) \, dx = 1 \qquad\qquad [2.2]$$

The integrand $P(x)$ is in general a function of x and defines the curve in Fig. 2.2; it is called the **probability density function** for x.

As indicated by equation [2.2] the total area under the curve bounded by the x-axis is unity, furthermore, the probability that a value of x lies in the interval $x_a < x < x_b$ is given by the area under the curve between x_a and x_b as shown in Fig. 2.2. Thus

$$P(x_a < x < x_b) = \int_{x_a}^{x_b} P(x) \, dx = A$$

Well-known discrete and continuous probability distributions are studied in the following two chapters.

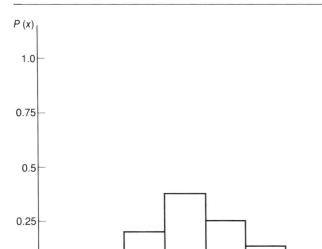

Fig 2.1 Discrete probability distribution, $\sum_{i=1}^{5} P(x_i) = 1$

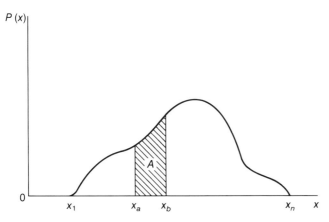

Fig 2.2 Continuous probability distribution, $\int_{x_1}^{x_n} P(x)\, \mathrm{d}x = 1$

Exercises

1. A contractor excavates for foundations in an area for which there are no available plans showing the position of existing services. The probabilities of cutting across the following services are as shown:

Water supply	: 0.12	Electricity	: 0.09
Drainage	: 0.06	Telephone cable	: 0.08
Gas	: 0.05		

Find the probability of cutting across

(a) one or more of these services
(b) both water supply and drainage
(c) either electricity or telephone cable.
[(a) 0.3421, (b) 0.0072, (c) 0.17]

2. A builder has acquired a large quantity of nuts and bolts of a certain standard size. If 5% of the nuts and 6% of the bolts are faulty, find the probability that when a nut and a bolt are chosen at randon,

(a) only the nut will be faulty
(b) only the bolt will be faulty
(c) at least one of them will be faulty
(d) neither of them will be faulty.
[(a) 0.047, (b) 0.057, (c) 0.107, (d) 0.893]

3. In a certain city a particular construction firm is engaged in four housing schemes, *A, B, C* and *D*. The houses can be classified as shown in Table 2.2.

Table 2.2

Bedrooms	Scheme			
	A	*B*	*C*	*D*
2	0	10	12	8
3	20	30	30	20
4	20	10	0	0

(a) Given that a prospective house buyer views a house at random, find the probability that
  (i)   it is on scheme C
  (ii)   it has at least 3 bedrooms
  (iii) it is on either scheme *A* or *B*.
(b) Given that a prospective buyer views two houses at random, find the probability that
  (i)   both are on scheme *D*
  (ii)   the first has 4 bedrooms and the second has 2 bedrooms
  (iii) the first is on either scheme *B* or *C* and the second has 3 bedrooms on scheme *A*.
[(a) 0.2625, 0.8125, 0.5625 (b) 0.0297, 0.0354, 0.0723]

4. The probabilities of a major accident occurring during the three phases of a construction project are 0.125, 0.2 and 0.1. Calculate the probability that

(a) an accident occurs on all three phases
(b) only one accident will occur
(c) at least one accident will occur.
[(a) 0.0025, (b) 0.3175, (c) 0.37]

Chapter 3

The binomial and
Poisson probability distributions

3.1 Introduction

An example of a discrete probability distribution is given by the **binomial probability distribution** (or **binomial distribution**). The random variable of this distribution is discrete and therefore can assume certain values only (actually, positive integer values). Because of this the binomial distribution is more applicable to problems involving *counted* data rather than *measured* data.

In construction the binomial distribution can be used to calculate, for example, the probability that a certain number of substandard components are present in a batch and also that a company will win a specified number of contracts in competitive tendering.

Under certain conditions the binomial distribution can be approximated by the Poisson probability distribution. This distribution can be used in problems concerned with site accidents and plant breakdowns.

3.2 The binomial distribution

The binomial distribution can be used whenever a series of n trials (where n is a positive integer) satisfies the following conditions:

(a) each trial has only two possible outcomes – success and failure;
(b) the outcomes of successive trials are independent (this condition is satisfied approximately when items are selected from a large population);
(c) the probability of success in a single trial is p and remains constant from trial to trial.

The required quantity is $P(x)$, the probability of x successes in n trials (x can take any of the values 0, 1, 2, ..., n). If the above conditions hold, then $P(x)$ is given by the binomial probability distribution,

$$P(x) = {_nC_x}\, p^x\, q^{n-x} \qquad [3.1]$$

where n = the number of trials
  x = the number of successes
  p = the probability of success in a single trial

$q = 1 - p$ (the probability of failure in a single trial)

and $_nC_x = \dfrac{n!}{x!(n-x)!}$

the number of ways x successes can occur in n trials.

The mean and standard deviation of a binomial distribution (i.e. the mean number of successes in n trials and the standard deviation) are given by

$$\mu = np \text{ and } \sigma = \sqrt{(npq)} \qquad\qquad [3.2]$$

The quantity np is called the **expectation** of success and so the mean of a binomial distribution gives the expected number of success in n trials.

To illustrate the use of the binomial distribution and to explain terms such as 'trial' and 'success' the following examples are presented.

Example 3.1

A large consignment of bags of cement is delivered to a building site. Given that the probability of a bag splitting due to handling and transportation is 0.15 find the probability of obtaining 0, 1, 2, 3 and 4 split bags when 4 bags are chosen at random.

In this problem 'trial' and 'success' mean the following;

trial   =   selecting a bag of cement
success   =   a split bag is selected
Hence n =   4
        p =   0.15
and q =   0.85.

The probability of obtaining, successively, $x = 0, 1, 2, 3$ and 4 successes is required.

Using equation [3.1] the probability of obtaining no split bags (i.e. $x = 0$) when 4 are chosen at random is

$P(0) = {}_4C_0 (0.15)^0(0.85)^4$
       $= 0.5220$

The probability of obtaining one split bag (i.e. $x = 1$) is

$P(1) = {}_4C_1 (0.15)^1(0.85)^3$
       $= 0.3685$

Similarly,
2 split bags: $P(2) = 0.0975$
3 split bags: $P(3) = 0.0115$
4 split bags: $P(4) = 0.0005$
Notice that the total probability is unity

i.e. $\displaystyle\sum_{x=0}^{4} P(x) = 1$ [3.3]

The calculated values of $P(x)$, $x = 0, 1, 2, 3$ and 4, constitute a discrete probability distribution and can be presented graphically as shown in Fig. 3.1.

If it is required to find, for example, the probability of obtaining at most two split bags (i.e. $x = 2$ or less) when 4 are chosen, then the addition law of probability can be used,

$$P(0 \text{ or } 1 \text{ or } 2) = P(0) + P(1) + P(2)$$
$$= 0.9880$$

Similarly the probability of obtaining at least one split bag (i.e. $x = 1$ or more) is

$P(1 \text{ or } 2 \text{ or } 3 \text{ or } 4)$
$= P(1) + P(2) + P(3) + P(4)$

or, using equation [3.3],

$$P(1 \text{ or } 2 \text{ or } 3 \text{ or } 4) = 1 - P(0)$$
$$= 0.4780$$

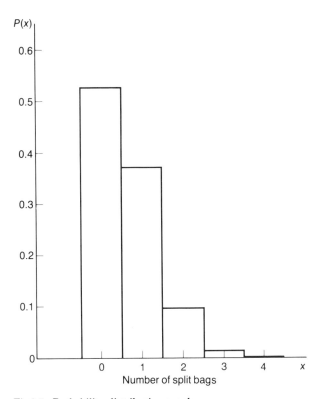

Fig 3.1 Probability distribution graph

Example 3.2

Two rival construction companies, A and B, compete for contracts. Last year the probabilities that a contract was won by A, by B and by neither were 0.45, 0.35 and 0.2 respectively. This year it is known that 5 contracts will be available for tender. Assuming the probabilities of A winning, of B winning and of neither winning remain the same as last year, find the probability that

(a) company A wins 3 contracts
(b) company B wins at most 1 contract
(c) two contracts are won by neither company A nor B.

Here   trial   = tendering for a contract
          success = winning a contract
and n = 5
company A: p_A = 0.45, q_A = 0.55
company B: p_B = 0.35, q_B = 0.65
neither: p_N = 0.2, q_N = 0.8

(a) The probability that company A wins three contracts (i.e. $x = 3$) is given by

$$P_A(3) = {_5}C_3 \, (0.45)^3 \, (0.55)^2$$
$$= 0.2757$$

(b) The probability that company B wins at most one contract (i.e. 1 or less) is given by

$$P_B(0 \text{ or } 1) = P_B(0) + P_B(1)$$
$$= {_5}C_0 \, (0.35)^0 \, (0.65)^5$$
$$+ {_5}C_1 \, (0.35)^1 \, (0.65)^4$$
$$= 0.1160 + 0.3124$$
$$= 0.4284$$

(c) The probability that two contracts (i.e. $x = 2$) are won by neither company A nor company B is given by

$$P_N(2) = {_5}C_2 \, (0.2)^2 \, (0.8)^3$$
$$= 0.2048$$

3.3   The Poisson distribution as an approximation

The calculations involved in the binomial distribution become very tedious and time-consuming when n is greater than about 10. In circumstances when n is large and p is small such that $np < 5$ the binomial distribution can be approximated by the **Poisson probability distribution** (or **Poisson distribution**).

The Poisson probability distribution is given by

$$P(x) = \frac{\lambda^x \, e^{-\lambda}}{x!} \qquad [3.4]$$

26

where $x = 0, 1, 2, \ldots$ and $\lambda = np$ (the expectation of success).

The mean and standard deviation of a Poisson distribution are, respectively,

$\mu = \lambda$ and $\sigma = \sqrt{\lambda}$

(which are consistent with equations [3.2] when p is small so that $q \approx 1$).

Example 3.3

The manufacturing process of a certain building component is such that 2% of all produced is substandard. Given that the manufacturer sends 150 components (chosen at random) to a building site, determine the probability that the site receives

(a)   5 substandard components
(b)   either 2 or 3 substandard components.

   In this problem,
trial   = selecting a component
success   = the component is substandard
n = 150
and p = 0.02.

   Now since $np < 5$ the Poisson approximation to the binomial distribution will be used with $\lambda = np = 3$.

(a)   Using equation [3.4]

$$P(5) = \frac{3^5 \, e^{-3}}{5!}$$

$$= 0.1008$$

(b)   Either 2 or 3 successes are required (i.e. $x = 2$ or 3) and so

$$P(2 \text{ or } 3) = P(2) + P(3)$$

Using equation [3.4] gives

$$P(2 \text{ or } 3) = 0.2240 + 0.2240$$
$$= 0.4480$$

3.4   *The Poisson distribution in its own right*

The Poisson distribution can also be used in its own right to determine probabilities associated with events which cannot be resolved using the binomial distribution.

   For example, if the mean accident rate on a particular building site is λ_0 per month then, with success denoting the occurrence of an accident, the expectation of success is $\lambda = \lambda_0$. Equation [3.4] can then be used to determine the probability that x accidents will occur in any given month.

   The binomial distribution cannot be applied to this problem because the number of times an accident did not occur is impossible to determine. Hence n is unknown, as are p and q.

Example 3.4

The plant on a certain building site suffers from (on average) two breakdowns per week. Determine the probability that a particular week will be free from stoppages due to plant failure.

Here the binomial distribution cannot be used because the number of times per week the plant did not break down is unknown.

The mean number of breakdowns per week is two. Hence $\lambda = 2$. Thus for no breakdowns (i.e. $x = 0$) equation [3.4] gives

$$P(0) = e^{-2} = 0.1353$$

Exercises

1. A dozen paving slabs are delivered to a site and, although they all look alike, there are three mixed in the delivery which are substandard and liable to crumble in heavy frost. Assuming only six of the slabs are laid, calculate the probability that none of the substandard ones are actually used.
[0.1780]

2. Building components produced by a manufacturer are such that 5% are substandard. Given that 10 are chosen at random, find the probability that

(a) one is substandard
(b) at most one is substandard
(c) either 1 or 2 are substandard
[(a) 0.3151, (b) 0.9138, (c) 0.3897]

3. In the past, two building contractors, A and B, have competed for 50 contracts. A won 30, B won 10 and 10 have gone to other contractors.

If three contracts are now up for tender and A and B are competing, what are the probabilities that,

(a) A will win all 3
(b) neither A nor B will win any
(c) B will win at least 1?
[(a) 0.216, (b) 0.008, (c) 0.488]

4. On a certain construction project the probability of a member of the labour force of 2000 men having an accident is 0.001. Find the probability that, during the project,

(a) 3 will have an accident
(b) more than 2 will have an accident
[(a) 0.1804, (b) 0.3233]

5. The mean number of breakdowns in plant on a construction site is 2.5 per five-day week. What is the probability of no breakdowns on a particular day? If the plant is used for 50 weeks, on how many days may two or more breakdowns be expected? [0.6065, 23 days]

6. A 500-page bill of quantities contains 100 discrepancies distributed at random. Find the probability that there will be two or more discrepancies on a page. [0.0176]

Chapter 4

The normal probability distribution

4.1   Introduction

As shown in the previous chapter, the variables of the binomial and Poisson distributions take positive integer values only. In contrast, the variable of the **normal probability distribution** (or **normal distribution**) can take any value on a number line; it is therefore a continuous random variable.

The normal distribution is one of the most important continuous probability distributions; this is because the relative frequency histogram of most measured quantities (e.g. weight, length, strength of material) is assumed to approach the normal distribution as the number of measurements increases and the class width decreases. Figure 4.1 illustrates this process when concrete cubes are tested for compressive strength.

A variable whose probability distribution is normal (or assumed normal) is said to be **normally distributed**. Hence, with reference to Fig. 4.1, concrete compressive strength can be considered normally distributed.

4.2   The normal distribution

The probability density function for the normal distribution is

$$P(x) = \frac{1}{\sigma\sqrt{(2\pi)}} e^{-(x-\mu)^2/(2\sigma^2)} \qquad\qquad [4.1]$$

A typical graph of equation [4.1] is shown in Fig. 4.2; it has the following properties:

(a)   the curve is bell shaped, symmetric about μ and never quite meets the x-axis
(b)   the total area bounded by the curve is 1
(c)   68.26% of the total area bounded by the curve is between

$$\mu - \sigma < x < \mu + \sigma$$

(d)   95.44% is between $\mu - 2\sigma < x < \mu + 2\sigma$
(e)   99.74% is between $\mu - 3\sigma < x < \mu + 3\sigma$

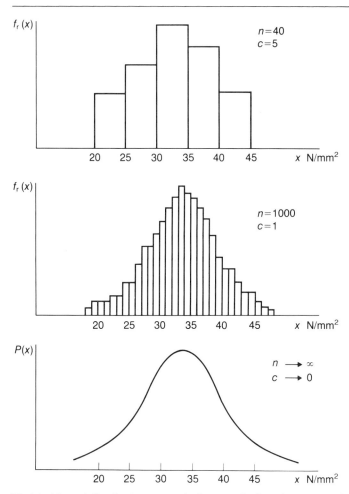

Fig 4.1 Normal distribution approached as sample size n increases and class width c decreases

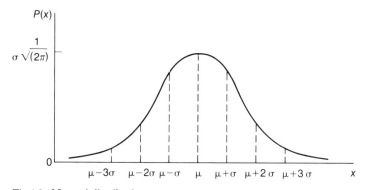

Fig 4.2 Normal distribution curve

31

As noted in Section 2.4, the probability that x has a value between x_a and x_b is given by

$$P(x_a < x < x_b) = \int_{x_a}^{x_b} \frac{1}{\sigma \sqrt{(2\pi)}} \, e^{-(x-\mu)^2/2\sigma^2} \, dx \qquad [4.2]$$

The fact that this integral is best evaluated numerically does not present a serious problem as a computer can be used. However, to cater for the infinite number of possible values of μ and σ (see Fig. 4.3) an infinite number of evaluations would be required. Hence in its present form equation [4.2] is not suitable in practice for calculating $P(x_a < x < x_b)$.

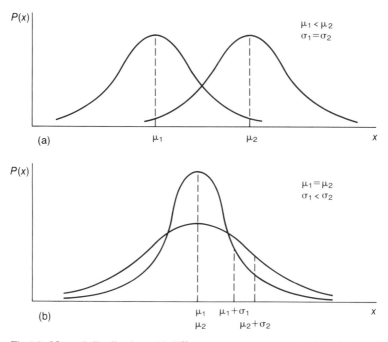

Fig 4.3 Normal distributions: (a) different means, same standard deviations; (b) same means, different standard deviations

A method of dealing with all normal distributions, irrespective of their values of μ and σ, is now presented.

4.3 The standard normal distribution

In order to evaluate equation [4.2] for all values of μ and σ the variable z is used, where

$$z = \frac{x - \mu}{\sigma} \qquad [4.3]$$

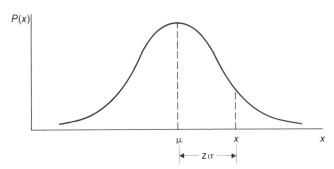

Fig 4.4 Normal distribution curve

and represents *the number of standard deviations the value x is away from the mean μ*, as shown in Fig. 4.4. The sign of z is positive or negative depending on whether the value x is to the right or left of μ, respectively. For example, if $z = 1.3$ then x is 1.3 standard deviations to the right of μ, that is, $x = \mu + 1.3\sigma$.

Equation [4.3] can be used to transform the normal distribution (given by equation [4.1]) from the x-variable to the z-variable as shown in Fig. 4.5. Notice that points $x = \mu + n\sigma (n = 0, \pm 1, \pm 2, ...)$ on the x-axis transform to the points $z = n$ on the z-axis. Hence equation [4.3] transforms a normal distribution with any value of μ and σ in the x-variable to one with $\mu = 0$ and $\sigma = 1$ in the z-variable.

The variable z is called the **standard normal variable** and the normal distribution with $\mu = 0$ and $\sigma = 1$ is called the **standard normal distribution**. The normal distribution properties (a) to (e) given in Section 4.2 still hold in the z-variable.

Returning to the problem of determining $P(x_a < x < x_b)$ in equation [4.2]; the use of equation [4.3] with $dz = dx/\sigma$ gives

$$P(x_a < x < x_b) = \int_{z_a}^{z_b} \frac{1}{\sqrt{(2\pi)}}\, e^{-z^2/2}\, dz$$

$$= P(z_a < z < z_b),$$

where $z_a = (x_a - \mu)/\sigma$, similarly for z_b. Again the integral is best evaluated numerically, but μ and σ have now been removed from the integrand and the limits are such that $-4 < z_a < z_b < 4$ in general.

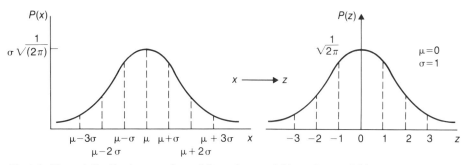

Fig 4.5 Normal distribution transformed from the x-variable to the z-variable

With $z_a = 0$ (i.e. $x_a = \mu$) and $z_b = z$ (i.e. $x_b = \mu + z\sigma$), where $z = 0(0.01)3.99$, the results of the integration are presented in Table A.1 in the Appendix. Hence the numbers in Table A.1 give the *areas* under the normal distribution curve for $\mu < x < \mu + z\sigma$, that is, they give $P(\mu < x < \mu + z\sigma)$. Furthermore, since the normal distribution curve is symmetric about μ the numbers in Table A.1 also give $P(\mu - z\sigma < x < \mu)$.

Example 4.1

Absorption tests on 500 bricks gave a mean absorption and standard deviation of 10.3% and 2.1% respectively. Determine the number of bricks with absorption

(a) between 8.9% and 11.1%
(b) greater than 15%.

The 500 absorption measurements are considered to be a population which is normally distributed with mean $\mu = 10.3\%$ and standard deviation $\sigma = 2.1\%$, as shown in Fig. 4.6.

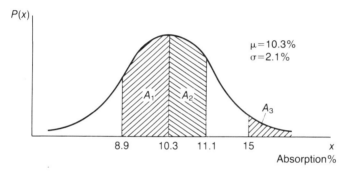

Fig 4.6 Normal distribution of absorption

(a) Converting 8.9 to the z-variable:

$$z = \frac{x - \mu}{\sigma} = \frac{8.9 - 10.3}{2.1} = -0.67$$

the negative sign merely indicates $8.9 < \mu$. Thus with $z = 0.67$ Table A.1 gives $A_1 = 0.2486$.

Converting 11.1 to the z-variable:

$$z = \frac{11.1 - 10.3}{2.1} = 0.38$$

and so $A_2 = 0.1480$. Thus the probability that a brick (chosen at random) has an absorption between 8.9% and 11.1% is

$$P(8.9 < x < 11.1) = A_1 + A_2$$
$$= 0.3966$$

Hence the number of bricks with absorption between 8.9% and 11.1% is 500 × 0.3966 = 198.3, i.e. 198 bricks.

(b)   Converting 15 to the z-variable,

$$z = \frac{15 - 10.3}{2.1} = 2.24$$

So Table A.1 gives the area under the normal curve contained between μ and 15 to be 0.4875. Thus

$$P(x > 15) = A_3$$
$$= 0.5 - 0.4875$$
$$= 0.0125$$

Hence the number of bricks with absorption greater than 15% is 500 × 0.0125 = 6.25, i.e. 6 bricks.

Example 4.2

Chip-board partition units are produced with a mean length of 750 mm and standard deviation 6 mm. Determine the rejection rate if the permissible length deviations are ± 15 mm (assume the lengths to be normally distributed).

Since the permissible deviations are ± 15 mm, the smallest and greatest acceptable lengths are 735 mm and 765 mm, respectively, as shown in Fig. 4.7.

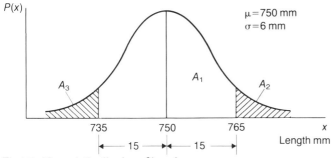

Fig 4.7   Normal distribution of length

Converting 765 to the z-variable:

$$z = \frac{765 - 750}{6} = 2.5$$

Thus Table A.1 gives $A_1 = 0.4938$
so $A_2 = 0.5 - 0.4938$
                        $= 0.0062$
Hence, by symmetry, $A_3 = 0.0062$
so $P(735 > x > 765) = A_2 + A_3$
                        $= 0.0124$

Thus 1.24% of all partition units have length x such that $735 > x > 765$, i.e. the rejection rate is 1.24%.

4.4   Strength of concrete

One of the major applications of the normal distribution to construction occurs in the specification of material strength, particularly that of concrete.

Factors that affect the compressive strength of concrete are numerous (e.g. water–cement ratio, type and grading of aggregates, curing conditions), hence strength variation is inevitable when concrete is produced over a period of time. In BS 5328 (1981) and CP 110 (1972) the variation is considered to be described by a normal distribution and a statistical approach to concrete strength is adopted.

In mix design it may seem obvious, for safety reasons, to specify that the concrete compressive strength must be above a certain value. However, the idea of an absolute minimum strength is incompatible with a statistical approach because the probability that a compressive strength value will occur that is lower than any specified minimum value is always non-zero. In other words, it is always possible (however remote) to obtain a compressive strength value lower than any specified minimum value.

Although no absolute minimum strength is possible BS 5328 defines a *statistical* 'minimum' strength called the **characteristic strength**, k, as

'that value of strength below which 5% of the population of all possible strength measurements of the specified concrete are expected to fall'.

An expression for k can be obtained by considering the normal distribution of all possible strength measurements (i.e. the population) as shown in Fig. 4.8. Since 5% of the population is below k this means $P(x < k) = 0.05$ and so area $A_1 = 0.05$. Hence area $A_2 = 0.45$ so that $P(k < x < \mu) = 0.45$. Thus Table A.1 gives the associated value of z to be -1.64 (negative because k is on the left of μ). Equation [4.3] then gives

$$-1.64 = \frac{k-\mu}{\sigma}$$

i.e.

$$k = \mu - 1.64\sigma \qquad [4.4]$$

It should be recognized that both the definition of k and its mathematical expression are purely theoretical statements; this is because μ and σ denote the mean compressive strength and standard deviation, respectively, of *all* concrete produced. Obviously, on a construction project, it is not possible to obtain strength measurements for absolutely all concrete produced; besides, none would be available for use if it was all destructively tested for compressive strength.

Unless specified the unknown population quantities μ and σ can be estimated by the values of $\hat{\mu}$ and $\hat{\sigma}$, respectively (given by equations [1.5] and [1.6], respectively). The values of $\hat{\mu}$ ($= \bar{x}$) and $\hat{\sigma}$ will be good estimates of μ and σ, respectively, provided enough test results are obtained (at least 40 are recommended). Thus a value for k can be obtained from

$$k = \bar{x} - 1.64\,\hat{\sigma} \qquad [4.5]$$

CP 110 defines the characteristic strength as

'that 28-day cube strength below which not more than 5% of the test results may be expected to fall'.

This definition also leads to equation [4.5]. Test results lower than the characteristic strength are called **defectives** and BS 5328 and CP 110 both define the value of k to be that compressive strength at the **5% defective level**.

The preceding discussion makes it clear that the characteristic strength is not an absolute minimum strength but a statistical 'minimum' strength associated with a specified defective level. Hence it is important to note that concrete with test results less than k *is acceptable* provided the 5% defective level is not exceeded. (Conditions imposed on the test results to ensure a defective level of at most 5% are considered in the next chapter.)

Equation [4.5], which applies only to a 5% defective level, can be generalized to

$$k = \bar{x} - |z|\hat{\sigma}$$

where the value of z (which will be negative) depends on the specified defective level.

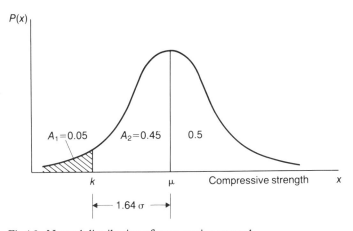

Fig 4.8 Normal distribution of compressive strength

For example, if the defective level is $m\%$ then area A_1 in Fig. 4.8 would now be $m/100$, so that area $A_2 = 0.5 - m/100$ and the associated value of z can be obtained from Table A.1.

Rearranging equation [4.4] to make μ the object, and generalizing, gives an equation used in concrete-mix design

$$\mu = k + |z|\sigma$$

where μ is the designed **target mean strength** and $|z|\sigma$ is called the **current margin** (or **margin**). In practice the standard deviation σ and characteristic strength k are both specified. Table 4.1 gives the characteristic strength values of various grades of concrete.

Table 4.1 Characteristic strength of concrete; after BS 5328

Concrete grade	Characteristic compressive strength, N/mm^2
C2.5	2.5
C5	5.0
C7.5	7.5
C10	10.0
C12.5	12.5
C15	15.0
C20	20.0
C25	25.0
C30	30.0
C35	35.0
C40	40.0
C45	45.0
C50	50.0
C55	55.0
C60	60.0

Example 4.3

40 concrete cubes from a mix were tested for compressive strength and found to have mean strength 32 N/mm^2 and standard deviation 6.5 N/mm^2.

(a) Decide whether or not the mix is acceptable if grade C20 was used (i.e. $k = 20$ N/mm^2).
(b) Determine the 'characteristic strength' if a 1% defective level is specified.

The compressive strength of the concrete comprising the mix (i.e. the population) is considered to be normally distributed (as shown in Fig. 4.9) with μ and σ estimated by $\hat{\mu}$ and $\hat{\sigma}$, respectively, where

$$\hat{\mu} = \bar{x} = 32 \text{ N/mm}^2$$

and

$$\hat{\sigma} = s\sqrt{\left(\frac{n}{n-1}\right)} = 6.5\sqrt{\left(\frac{40}{39}\right)}$$

$$= 6.58 \text{ N/mm}^2$$

However, attention is drawn to the fact that in construction the sample standard deviation is sometimes calculated using the expression on the right-hand side of equation [1.6] rather than that of equation [1.4] (i.e. with a denominator of $n-1$ instead of n); if this was the case here, then σ would be estimated by $\hat{\sigma} = 6.5$ N/mm^2.

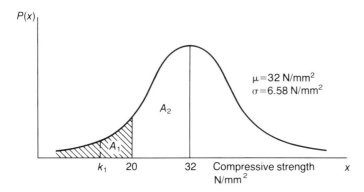

Fig 4.9 Normal distribution of compressive strength

(a) Converting 20 to the z-variable:

$$z = \frac{20-32}{6.58} = -1.82$$

so $z = 1.82$ gives $A_2 = 0.4656$. Thus

$$P(x < 20) = A_1$$
$$= 0.5 - 0.4656$$
$$= 0.0344$$

Hence the defective level is 3.44%, which is less than the 5% maximum, and so the mix is acceptable.

(b) If k_1 is the 'characteristic strength' at the 1% defective level then $P(x < k_1) = 0.01$. Thus $P(k_1 < x < \mu) = 0.49$ and so $z = -2.33$. Hence,

$$k_1 = \mu - |z|\sigma$$
$$= 32 - (2.33 \times 6.58)$$
$$= 16.67 \text{ N/mm}^2$$

Example 4.4

If grade C25 concrete with standard deviation 6 N/mm² is to be used over a period of time on a construction project. Calculate the current margin and target mean strength.

Concrete of grade C25 has characteristic strength $k = 25$ N/mm². Also, as shown in Section 4.4, a defective level of 5% gives $z = -1.64$. Thus the current margin is given by

$$|z|\sigma = 1.64 \times 6 = 9.84 \text{ N/mm}^2$$

and the target mean strength is therefore

$$\mu = k + (\text{current margin})$$
$$= 25 + 9.84$$
$$= 34.84 \text{ N/mm}^2$$

4.5   Normal probability paper

If a continuous variable x is normally distributed as shown in Fig. 4.10 (a), then Fig. 4.10 (b) illustrates the **percentage cumulative probability**, $C(x)$, for any value of x. With reference to Fig. 4.10 (b) notice that if $A_1 = P(x < x_1)$ then $C(x_1) = (100A_1)\% = (100P(x < x_1))\%$; hence $C(\mu) = 50\%$ and $C(\mu + \sigma) - C(\mu) = 34.13\%$ so that $C(\mu + \sigma) = 84.13\%$. Furthermore, if $C(x)$ and x are plotted on normal probability paper as shown in Fig. 4.10(c) (the horizontal x-axis retains its linear scale while the vertical $C(x)$-axis is transformed to a nonlinear probability scale), then the 'S' curve of Fig. 4.10 (b) becomes a straight line.

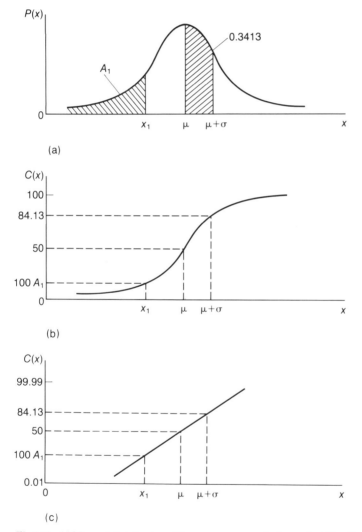

(a)

(b)

(c)

Fig 4.10   (a) Normal distribution; (b) percentage cumulative probability distribution; (c) normal probability paper

As will be demonstrated in the following example, normal probability paper can be used as a graphical test of normality and to determine the mean and standard deviation of a distribution.

Example 4.5

Compressive strength measurements obtained from concrete cubes taken from a mix are displayed as a frequency distribution in Table 4.2. Verify graphically that the compressive strength of the test cubes is normally distributed and hence determine the mean strength and standard deviation of the mix.

Table 4.3 is now constructed using the data in Table 4.2. Entries in the first and second columns of Table 4.3 are upper class boundaries and cumulative frequencies, respectively; those in the third column are given by

percentage cumulative probability

$$= \frac{\text{cumulative frequency}}{\text{total frequency}} \times 100\%$$

Corresponding entries in the first and third columns of Table 4.3 are then plotted on normal probability paper, as shown in Fig. 4.11, where it is seen that each point lies approximately on the drawn straight line. Hence the compressive strength distribution of the test cubes can be considered normal.

Since the straight line in Fig. 4.11 applies to the compressive strengths of the test cubes only (not the entire mix), the graphically obtained values of the mean and standard deviation are those for $\bar{x}$ and s, respectively (as opposed to μ and σ, respectively).

However, since the graphical method gives only approximate values, μ and σ can be estimated by $\bar{x}$ and s, respectively, that is $\hat{\mu} = \bar{x}$ and $\hat{\sigma} = s$ (here there is no merit in

Table 4.2 Frequency distribution of compressive strengths	
Compressive strength N/mm²	*Number of cubes*
19−20	1
21−22	4
23−24	5
25−26	6
27−28	8
29−30	10
31−32	18
33−34	9
35−36	7
37−38	6
39−40	5
41−42	1
Total	80

Table 4.3 Calculation of percentage cumulative probabilities		
Compressive strength N/mm²	*Cumulative frequency*	*Percentage cumulative probability*
less than 20.5	1	1.25
less than 22.5	5	6.25
less than 24.5	10	12.5
less than 26.5	16	20
less than 28.5	24	30
less than 30.5	34	42.5
less than 32.5	52	65
less than 34.5	61	76.25
less than 36.5	68	85
less than 38.5	74	92.5
less than 40.5	79	98.75
less than 42.5	80	100

41

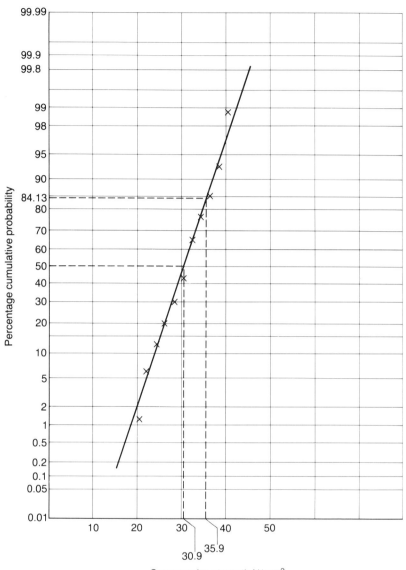

Fig 4.11 Normal probability paper

using $\hat{\sigma} = s\sqrt{[n/(n-1)]}$). Hence, from Fig. 4.11,

$$C(30.9) = 50\%$$
i.e. $$\hat{\mu} = 30.9 \text{ N/mm}^2$$
and $$C(35.9) = 84.13\%$$
i.e. $$\hat{\mu} + \hat{\sigma} = 35.9 \text{ N/mm}^2$$
so $$\hat{\sigma} = 5.0 \text{ N/mm}^2$$

42

Fig. 4.11 can also be used to estimate the defective level. For example, if the concrete is of grade C20 then the graph gives a defective level of approximately 2%.

4.6 Structural design philosophy

In CP 110 (1972) it is recognized that no structure can be made completely safe but only that the probability of failure may be reduced to an acceptably low level.

As stated in CP 110,

'the purpose of design is the achievement of acceptable probabilities that the structure being designed will not become unfit for the use for which it is required, i.e. that it will not reach a limit state',

indeed, the philosophy of design (called **limit state design**) is based on probability theory and the use of statistical methods to analyse variations in the loads on structures and in the strengths of materials used.

CP 110 gives the limit states which must be considered in design together with their requirements:

(a) *The ultimate limit state*: The strength of the structure should be sufficient to withstand the design loads taking due account of the possibility of overturning or buckling;

(b) *The serviceability limit states:* In addition to strength requirements CP 110 recognizes that excessive deflection, cracking and vibration can cause a structure to become unfit for use. Requirements on these causes are termed the serviceability limit states.

The use of statistics to analyse variations in concrete strength has been discussed in Section 4.4. To include other construction materials equation [4.4] can be generalized to

$$f_k = f_m - 1.64\,\sigma_f \qquad\qquad [4.6]$$

where f_k, f_m and σ_f denote the characteristic strength of the material, the mean strength and standard deviation, respectively. Table 4.4 gives characteristic strength values for steel (see also Table 4.1).

Table 4.4 Characteristic strength of steel; after CP 110

Designation	Nominal sizes mm	Characteristic strength N/mm^2
Hot-rolled mild steel	all sizes	250
Hot-rolled high-yield steel	all sizes	410
Cold-worked high-yield steel	$\leqslant 16$	460
Cold-worked high-yield steel	> 16	425
Hard-drawn steel wire	$\leqslant 12$	485

43

As with the characteristic strength of material, **characteristic loads** on a structure must also be considered in design, i.e. loads which have a low probability of being *exceeded* during the life of the structure. CP 110 lists the following characteristic loads:

(a) *The characteristic dead load, G_k:* This is the weight of the structure complete with finishes, fixtures and partitions.
(b) *The characteristic imposed load, Q_k:* Load due to furniture, occupants, machinery, vehicles, etc.
(c) *The characteristic wind load, W_k:* Load obtained from a wind whose speed is exceeded only once in a specified number of years.

Ideally the characteristic loads should be determined using the mean and standard deviation of a probability distribution (as is the case with the characteristic strength, see equation [4.6]). However, because of insufficient relevant statistical data it is not possible to do this and so the characteristic loads used in practice are based on experience. Limit state design is therefore only a semi-probabilistic method.

Nevertheless, if the loads experienced by a structure are assumed to be normally distributed, then the characteristic load could be defined as that load above which not more than 5% of the loads fall when all the loads likely to be applied to the structure during its lifetime are considered. Thus, with reference to the normal distribution of loads as shown in Fig. 4.12,

$$F_k = F_m + 1.64 \, \sigma_F$$

where F_k, F_m and σ_F denote the characteristic load, mean load and standard deviation, respectively. In other words, just as the characteristic strength, f_k, is the statistical 'minimum' strength of the material (at the 5% defective level), the characteristic load, F_k, is the statistical 'maximum' load experienced by the structure (at the 5% defective level).

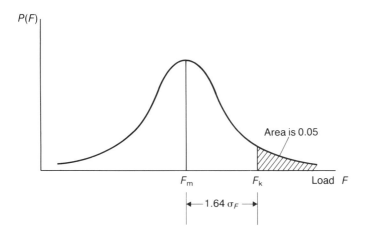

Fig 4.12 Normal distribution of load

The probability that a structure experiences a load greater than F_k is small, similarly for the probability that a material has strength below f_k (0.05 in both cases, by definition). Thus the probability that both events occur simultaneously, so that structural failure may occur, is extremely small (but non-zero).

Although already remote, the possibility of structural failure can be reduced by considering the 'maximum' load and 'minimum' strength to be $\gamma_f F_k$ and f_k/γ_m, respectively (where, in general, γ_f and $\gamma_m \geqslant 1$). The values of $\gamma_f F_k$ and f_k/γ_m are more conservative than their respective characteristic values and are therefore used for design purposes. The quantities $\gamma_f F_k$ and f_k/γ_m are called the **design load** and **design strength**, respectively, where γ_f and γ_m are the **partial safety factors** for loads and material strength, respectively. The use of two separate factors of safety allows uncertainties in the estimation of loading and in the performance of materials to be assessed separately. Table 4.5 gives values of γ_m for concrete and steel.

As previously stated, there are several characteristic loads; G_k, Q_k and W_k, and so a partial safety factor may apply to each; γ_{fG}, γ_{fQ} and γ_{fW}, respectively. Thus, in general, the design load is given by

$$\text{Design load} = \gamma_{fG}\, G_k + \gamma_{fQ}\, Q_k + \gamma_{fW}\, W_k$$

Table 4.6 gives the design loads for various load combinations.

The following simple example illustrates the use of partial safety factors in limit state design.

Table 4.5 Partial safety factors for material strength; after CP 110

Limit state	Concrete	Steel
Ultimate	1.5	1.15
Serviceability		
Deflection	1.0	1.0
Cracking	1.3	1.0

Table 4.6 Design loads for various load combinations; after CP 110

Limit state	Load combination	Design loads
Ultimate	Dead + imposed	$1.4G_k + 1.6Q_k$
	Dead + wind	$0.9G_k + 1.4Q_k$
	Dead + imposed + wind	$1.2(G_k + Q_k + W_k)$
Serviceability	Dead + imposed	$1.0(G_k + Q_k)$
	Dead + wind	$1.0(G_k + W_k)$
	Dead + imposed + wind	$1.0G_k + 0.8(Q_k + W_k)$

Example 4.6

Use limit state design to determine the cross-sectional area of a mild steel cable which supports a total dead load of 2.5 kN and imposed load of 1.5 kN.

The relevant data is,

the characteristic dead load $G_k = 2500$ N
the characteristic imposed load $Q_k = 1500$ N
and from Tables 4.4. and 4.5, respectively,
the characteristic yield stress (strength) of mild steel

$$f_k = 250 \text{ N/mm}^2$$

and the partial safety factor for steel strength,

$$\gamma_m = 1.15$$

Hence the design stress $= f_k/\gamma_m$
$$= 217.4 \text{ N/mm}^2$$

Using Table 4.6,

design load $= 1.4G_k + 1.6Q_k$
$$= 5900 \text{ N}$$

and so,

$$\text{cross-sectional area} = \frac{\text{design load}}{\text{design stress}} = 27.1 \text{ mm}^2$$

Exercises

1. The mean compressive strength and standard deviation of 200 concrete cubes from mixes of the same design were found to be 32.4 N/mm² and 6.3 N/mm², respectively. Determine,

(a) the percentage of cubes that had strength between 30 N/mm² and 35 N/mm²
(b) the number of cubes that had strength between 34 N/mm² and 37 N/mm²
(c) the number of cubes that had strength less than 27 N/mm².
    [(a) 30.71%, (b) 34, (c) 39]

2. Steel beams are manufactured with mean length 5 m and standard deviation 5 mm. Determine

(a) the rejection rate if the permissible length deviations are ± 12 mm
(b) the permissible length deviations if a rejection rate of 5% is specified.
    [(a) 1.64%, (b) ± 9.3 mm]

3. Given that grade C20 concrete with standard deviation 6.5 N/mm² is to be used on a construction project, calculate the current margin and the target mean strength.
[10.66 N/mm², 30.66 N/mm²]

4. Calculate the current margin and 'characteristic strength' of concrete with a specified defective level of 2.5% and a required target mean strength of 33 N/mm². The standard deviation of the concrete is 6.8 N/mm².
[13.33 N/mm², 19.67 N/mm²]

5. The following results refer to the length measurements of 100 lengths of timber (of the same standard type) delivered to a building site.

Table 4.7

Length mm	Number of lengths
3000–3010	1
3010–3020	2
3020–3030	11
3030–3040	18
3040–3050	34
3050–3060	20
3060–3070	9
3070–3080	3
3080–3090	1
3090–3100	1

Use normal probability paper to determine the mean and standard deviation of the length distribution.

[3045.6 mm, 14.8 mm]

6. Concrete cubes from a mix were tested for compressive strength and gave the following results.

Table 4.8

Compressive strength N/mm^2	Number of cubes
23–25	6
26–28	15
29–31	28
32–34	25
35–37	12
38–40	4

Use normal probability paper to find the mean strength, standard deviation and characteristic strength of the mix.

[31.1 N/mm^2, 3.7 N/mm^2, 25.0 N/mm^2]

Chapter 5

Normal sampling distributions

5.1 Introduction

Often when a large number of items are considered (i.e. a population) it is impractical for reasons of time, effort, cost, or use of a destructive test to measure the required property (e.g. length, weight, compressive strength) of each individual item. Hence, in practice, only n items are measured where the value of n is optimized with respect to the time, effort involved and cost of the measuring process.

The n items are called *a sample of size n* and should be chosen at random so that they are representative of the population. If $n \geqslant 30$ then the sample is called a **large sample**, whereas if $n < 30$ it is a **small sample**.

Once samples of size n are obtained from a population (a process called *sampling*) they can be used in the following contexts:

(a) to obtain information about sample properties;
(b) to obtain information about population properties (see Chapter 6);
(c) to make statistical decisions about a population (see Chapter 7).

Context (a) only is considered in this chapter together with, in general, large samples. However, before proceeding further a general equation is now formulated.

If large samples are continually drawn from a population and the value of a certain property, Q, of each sample is recorded, then Fig. 5.1 illustrates the assumed normal distribution of sample property Q. The mean and standard deviation of this sampling distribution are denoted by μ_Q and σ_Q, respectively, and since a normal sampling distribution is assumed, then properties (a) to (e) of Section 4.2 are valid with the Q-variable.

With reference to Fig. 5.1, z denotes the number of standard deviations the value Q is away from the distribution mean μ_Q, therefore $z\sigma_Q = Q - \mu_Q$, so that

$$z = \frac{Q - \mu_Q}{\sigma_Q}$$

Hence, in general, the standard normal variable z can be expressed as

$$z = \frac{\text{variable value - mean}}{\text{standard deviation}} \qquad [5.1]$$

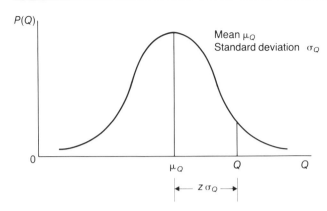

Fig 5.1   Normal distribution of sample property Q

where 'variable value', 'mean' and 'standard deviation' are those of whatever normal distribution is in question.

5.2   The distribution of sample means

Consider a theoretical infinite population of, for example, compressive strength measurements, x_i, $i = 1, 2, 3, ...$, with mean and standard deviation given by μ and σ respectively. Moreover, suppose that samples of size $n \geqslant 30$ are continually taken (with or without replacement) from the population and the mean compressive strength of each sample, $\bar{x}_i$, is calculated (here the subscript i denotes the ith sample of n strength measurements) as shown in Fig. 5.2.

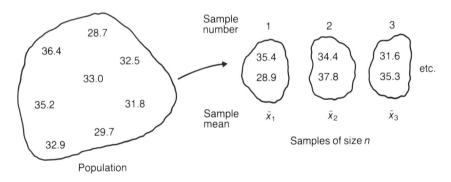

Fig 5.2   Sampling from a population

Hence an infinite collection of mean compressive strengths, $\bar{x}_i$, $i = 1, 2, 3, ...$, is generated. Furthermore, the probability distribution of these mean compressive strengths, that is, **the distribution of sample means**, is approximately normal with

49

mean and standard deviation denoted by $\mu_{\bar{x}}$ and $\sigma_{\bar{x}}$, respectively, where

$$\mu_{\bar{x}} = \mu \qquad\qquad [5.2]$$

and

$$\sigma_{\bar{x}} = \frac{\sigma}{\sqrt{n}} \qquad\qquad [5.3]$$

Provided the sampling is with replacement equations [5.2] and [5.3] are still true with a finite population. However, if samples of size $n \geqslant 30$ are drawn without replacement from a finite population of size n_p, then the distribution of sample means is still approximately normal with $\mu_{\bar{x}} = \mu$ but the standard deviation is now given by

$$\sigma_{\bar{x}} = \frac{\sigma}{\sqrt{n}} \sqrt{\left(\frac{n_p - n}{n_p - 1}\right)} \qquad\qquad [5.4]$$

With reference to equations [5.2] – [5.4] the following points are noted.

(a) The accuracy of the approximation to a normal distribution by the distribution of sample means improves as the sample size n increases.
(b) Equation [5.4] reduces to equation [5.3] as the population size n_p increases because $\dfrac{n_p - n}{n_p - 1}$ approaches 1.
(c) Equations [5.2] – [5.4] are in fact valid with any sample size and population distribution, but the distribution of sample means is not normal in all cases.
(d) If the population distribution is normal then the distribution of sample means is normal for both large and small samples.

A normal population distribution and its normal distribution of sample means are shown in Fig. 5.3 where properties (a) to (e) of Section 4.2 also hold with the $\bar{x}$-variable.

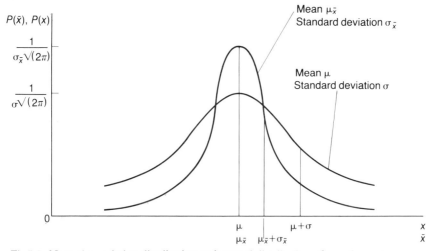

Fig 5.3 Normal population distribution and normal distribution of sample means

The general sample property Q of the previous section is now denoted by the sample mean $\bar{x}$ (mean compressive strength, for example). Furthermore, for the distribution of sample means, equation [5.1] gives

$$z = \frac{\bar{x} - \mu_{\bar{x}}}{\sigma_{\bar{x}}} \qquad [5.5]$$

where $\mu_{\bar{x}} = \mu$ and $\sigma_{\bar{x}}$ and is given by equation [5.3] (or equation [5.4] if the sampling is without replacement from a finite population).

Example 5.1

Analysis of 150 compressive strength results gave a mean strength of 32 N/mm^2 and standard deviation 6.5 N/mm^2. Given that 10 samples of 12 results are considered, find the number of samples with mean strength greater than 33 N/mm^2.

The relevant data is

population mean	μ	= 32 N/mm^2
population standard deviation	σ	= 6.5 N/mm^2
population size	n_p	= 150
sample size	n	= 12
number of samples	N	= 10

Although the sample size is small ($n < 30$) the distribution of sample mean strengths is normal because the population of individual strengths is considered normal.

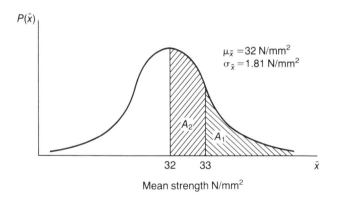

Fig 5.4 Normal distribution of sample mean compressive strength

Here the sampling is without replacement from a finite population so that the normal distribution of sample mean strengths (see Fig. 5.4) has mean and standard deviation given by, respectively,

$$\mu_{\bar{x}} = \mu = 32 \text{ N/mm}^2$$

and

$$\sigma_{\bar{x}} = \frac{\sigma}{\sqrt{n}} \sqrt{\left(\frac{n_p - n}{n_p - 1}\right)}$$

$$= \frac{6.5}{\sqrt{12}} \sqrt{\left(\frac{150 - 12}{150 - 1}\right)}$$

$$= 1.81 \text{ N/mm}^2$$

With reference to Fig. 5.4,

$$P(\bar{x} > 33) = A_1 = 0.5 - A_2$$

Converting 33 to the z-variable:

$$z = \frac{\bar{x} - \mu_{\bar{x}}}{\sigma_{\bar{x}}} = \frac{33 - 32}{1.81} = 0.55$$

Thus area $A_2 = 0.2088$ so that

$$P(\bar{x} > 33) = 0.2912$$

Hence the number of samples with mean strength greater than 33 N/mm² is $N \times 0.2912 = 2.912$, i.e. 3 samples.

Example 5.2

Asbestos-cement sheets are manufactured with mean length 2400 mm and standard deviation 3 mm. Given that 20 batches consisting of 3 dozen sheets are considered, determine

(a) the probability that a batch (chosen at random) has mean length between 2399.5 mm and 2400.6 mm

(b) the number of batches with mean length less than 2399.3 mm.

In this example the relevant data are

population mean	μ	= 2400 mm
population standard deviation	σ	= 3 mm
sample size	n	= 36
number of samples	N	= 20

The population of sheet lengths (which needn't be normally distributed) is considered infinite and the sampling is without replacement. Thus, using equations [5.2] and [5.3], the mean and standard deviation of the normal distribution of sample mean lengths (see Fig. 5.5) are, respectively,

$$\mu_{\bar{x}} = \mu = 2400 \text{ mm}$$

and

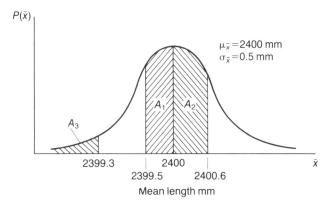

Fig 5.5 Normal distribution of sample mean length

$$\sigma_{\bar{x}} = \frac{\sigma}{\sqrt{n}} = \frac{3}{\sqrt{36}} = 0.5 \text{ mm}$$

(a) Converting 2399.5 to the z-variable:

$$z = \frac{\bar{x} - \mu_{\bar{x}}}{\sigma_{\bar{x}}} = \frac{2399.5 - 2400}{0.5} = -1$$

Thus with $z = 1$ area $A_1 = 0.3413$.
  Converting 2400.6 to the z-variable:

$$z = \frac{2400.6 - 2400}{0.5} = 1.2$$

and so area $A_2 = 0.3849$. Hence the probability that a batch has mean length between 2399.5 mm and 2400.6 mm is

$$P(2399.5 < \bar{x} < 2400.6) = A_1 + A_2$$
$$= 0.7262$$

(b) Converting 2399.3 to the z-variable:

$$z = \frac{2399.3 - 2400}{0.5} = -1.4$$

Hence with $z = 1.4$ the area under the normal curve between 2399.3 and 2400 (see Fig. 5.5) is 0.4192. Therefore,

$$P(\bar{x} < 2399.3) = A_3$$
$$= 0.5 - 0.4192$$
$$= 0.0808$$

Thus the number of batches with mean length less than 2399.3 mm is $N \times 0.0808 = 1.616$, that is, 2 batches.

5.3   The compliance criteria

As noted in Section 4.4, BS 5328 (1981) and CP 110 (1972) both define the characteristic strength as that compressive strength at the 5% defective level. However, with a specified characteristic strength, the problem arises as to how to ensure that the 5% defective level is not exceeded. In order to achieve this conditions are imposed on the compressive strength results obtained from test cubes. These conditions are called the **compliance criteria** and CP 110 states that compliance with the specified characteristic strength may be assumed if:

(a)   the average strength determined from any group of four consecutive test cubes exceeds the specified characteristic strength by not less than 0.5 times the current margin, and
(b)   each individual result is greater than 85% of the specified characteristic strength.

The above compliance criteria are now investigated in terms of statistics.

Criterion (a)   This criterion relates to the distribution of sample means since the mean strength of four test cubes is considered. Although the sample size is small ($n = 4$) the population distribution of individual cube strengths is considered to be normal so that the distribution of sample mean strengths is also normal (by point (d) of Section 5.2).
    If the mean compressive strengths of samples of four consecutive concrete cubes are denoted by $\bar{x}_i$, $i = 1, 2, 3, ...$, then the condition expressed in criterion (a) is

$$\bar{x}_i - k \nless 0.5 \times \text{(current margin)}$$

where the current margin at the 5% defective level of individual cube strengths is $1.64\,\sigma$ (cf. Section 4.4). Thus criterion (a) can be written as

$$\bar{x}_i - k \geqslant 0.82\,\sigma$$

The above mathematical expression is now shown to be equivalent to specifying that the concrete associated with a particular sample of four cubes will be accepted provided the mean strength of the four cubes is not less than $k_{\bar{x}}$, where $k_{\bar{x}}$ denotes the statistical minimum strength (at the 5% level) for the mean strengths of four cubes.
    Consider the normal distribution of sample mean strengths as shown in Fig. 5.6. Since $P(\bar{x}_i < k_{\bar{x}}) = 0.05$, areas A_1 and A_2 are 0.05 and 0.45, respectively. Hence $z = -1.64$ and so, using equation [5.5], $\mu_{\bar{x}} - k_{\bar{x}} = 1.64\sigma_{\bar{x}}$. Now if each $\bar{x}_i$, $i = 1, 2, 3, ...$, is not less than $k_{\bar{x}}$ then

$$\mu_{\bar{x}} - \bar{x}_i \leqslant 1.64\,\sigma_{\bar{x}}$$

Furthermore, using equations [5.2] *and* [5.3] *with $n = 4$, the above inequality becomes*

$$\mu - \bar{x}_i \leqslant 0.82\sigma \qquad [5.6]$$

Finally, equation [4.4] gives $\mu = k + 1.64\,\sigma$, which, when substituted into inequality [5.6], yields the first compliance criterion; $\bar{x}_i - k \geqslant 0.82\sigma$.

Criterion (b)   Each individual compressive strength result, x_i, $i = 1, 2, 3, \ldots$, is

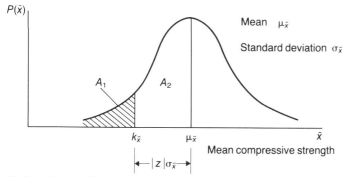

Fig 5.6   Normal distribution of sample mean compressive strength

required to be such that $x_i > 0.85k$ (where k denotes the specified characteristic strength).

Since, by definition, 5% of results are expected to be less than k, *then clearly the* probability of $x_i < 0.85k$ (i.e. area A_1 in Fig. 5.7) is less than 0.05. In fact

$$P(x_i < 0.85k) = A_1$$
$$= 0.5 - A_2$$

where area A_2 is obtained from Table A.1 (in Appendix) with $z = (x - \mu)/\sigma$, that is, since $x = 0.85k$ and $\mu = k + 1.64\sigma$,

$$z = -(0.15 \frac{k}{\sigma} + 1.64)$$

Hence, for example, if $k = 20$ N/mm² and $\sigma = 6$ N/mm², then $z = -2.14$ and so $A_2 = 0.4838$. Thus

$$P(x_i < 0.85k) = 0.0162$$

In other words, the rejection rate for individual cubes is 1.62%.

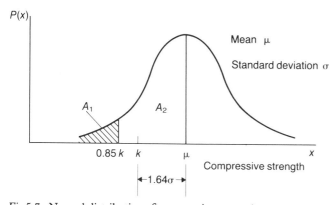

Fig 5.7   Normal distribution of compressive strength

To summarize, the CP 110 compliance criteria are, in terms of inequalities,

(a) $\bar{x}_i \geqslant k + 0.82\sigma$
(b) $x_i > 0.85k$

In comparison BS 5328 states, for concrete of grade C20 and above, that compliance with the characteristic strength shall be assumed if

(a) the average strength determined from any group of four consecutive test results exceeds the specified characteristic strength by 3 N/mm², and
(b) the strength determined from any test result is not less than the specified characteristic strength minus 3 N/mm².

In terms of inequalities the BS 5328 compliance criteria are

(a) $\bar{x}_i > k + 3$
(b) $x_i \geqslant k - 3$

which, compared with those CP 110, are different expressions and independent of σ. Hence, for example, if grade C20 concrete is considered, then the CP 110 compliance criteria impose stronger conditions when $\sigma > 3.66$ N/mm.

The compliance criteria adopted by CP 110 and BS 5328 have the purpose of ensuring, for a specified characteristic strength, a defective level of at most 5%.

However, as stated in Section 4.4, concrete with compressive strength less than the characteristic strength is acceptable provided the 5% defective level is not exceeded. Hence with any compliance criteria there is *always* the possibility that concrete of the required quality is indicated as not complying and also that concrete of inferior quality is accepted. This is a consequence of the statistical approach to concrete strength.

The effect of compliance criteria on the probability of rejecting (accepting) good concrete (inferior concrete) is investigated in Chapter 7.

Example 5.3

(a) Calculate the probability of grade C30 concrete failing the CP 110 85% compliance criterion when it is designed for 2% of compressive strength results to fall below the characteristic strength. The specified standard deviation is 7 N/mm².
(b) Calculate the probability of the concrete in part (a) failing the CP 110 mean-of-four compliance criterion.

(a) Concrete of grade C30 has characteristic strength 30 N/mm². Usually 5% of the test results would be expected to fall below this strength, but here the concrete mix is designed so that only 2% are less than 30 N/mm². Hence $k_2 = 30$ N/mm², where k_2 denotes the 'characteristic strength' at the 2% defective level.

If x denotes compressive strength, then since $P(x < k_2) = 0.02$, area $A_1 = 0.02$, as shown in Fig. 5.8. Hence area $A_2 = 0.48$ and so $z = -2.05$. The target mean strength is therefore

$$\mu = k_2 + |z|\,\sigma$$
$$= 30 + 2.05 \times 7$$
$$= 44.35 \text{ N/mm}^2$$

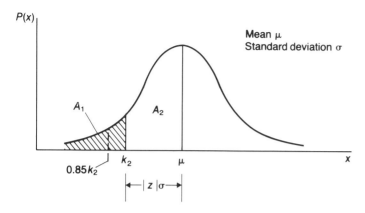

Fig 5.8   Normal distribution of compressive strength

Now the probability that an individual test result is less than $0.85k_2$, i.e. 25.5 N/mm², is given by

$$P(x < 0.85k_2) = 0.5 - P(0.85k_2 < x < \mu)$$

(see Fig. 5.8), that is,

$$P(x < 25.5) = 0.5 - P(25.5 < x < 44.35)$$

Converting 25.5 to the z-variable

$$z = \frac{25.5 - 44.35}{7} = -2.69$$

Hence $P(25.5 < x < 44.35) = 0.4964$ and
$P(x < 25.5) = 0.0036$

i.e. the rejection rate for individual cubes is 0.36%.

(b)   With the mean-of-four criterion the distribution of sample means must be considered, as shown in Fig. 5.9, where $\bar{x}$ denotes the mean of four test results.

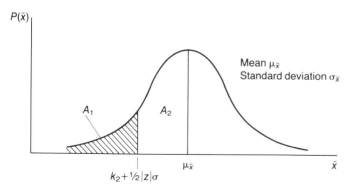

Fig 5.9   Normal distribution of sample mean compressive strength

The mean and standard deviation of the normal distribution of sample means are given by, respectively,

$$\mu_{\bar{x}} = \mu = 44.35 \text{ N/mm}^2$$

and

$$\sigma_{\bar{x}} = \frac{\sigma}{\sqrt{n}} = \frac{7}{\sqrt{4}} = 3.5 \text{ N/mm}^2$$

Now the mean strength of four results will not comply if $\bar{x} <$ (characteristic strength) $+ \frac{1}{2}$ (current margin) that is,

$$\bar{x} < k_2 + \tfrac{1}{2} \mid z \mid \sigma$$

where $k_2 = 30 \text{ N/mm}^2$ and $\mid z \mid \sigma = 2.05 \times 7 = 14.35 \text{ N/mm}^2$ (the current margin is shown in Fig. 5.8).

The probability that $\bar{x} < k_2 + \frac{1}{2} \mid z \mid \sigma$ is given by area A_1 in Fig. 5.9, where $A_1 = 0.5 - A_2$ and $A_2 = P(k_2 + \frac{1}{2} \mid z \mid \sigma < \bar{x} < \mu_{\bar{x}})$. Hence

$$P(\bar{x} < 37.18) = 0.5 - P(37.18 < \bar{x} < 44.35)$$

Converting 37.18 to the z-variable:

$$z = \frac{\bar{x} - \mu_{\bar{x}}}{\sigma_{\bar{x}}} = \frac{37.18 - 44.35}{3.5} = -2.05$$

so with $z = 2.05$ area $A_2 = 0.4798$, thus

$$P(\bar{x} < 37.18) = 0.5 - 0.4798$$
$$= 0.0202$$

That is, the rejection rate for the mean of four results is 2.02%.

5.4   The distribution of sample mean differences

In the sampling considered so far in this chapter each sample was taken from a single population. In this section a particular property of a sample is compared with that of another sample which may be from a different population.

The need to compare sample properties can occur, for example, when samples are taken from the same population but have a particular property measured by two different processes or devices, or when the same measuring process or device is used on samples from two populations.

An application in construction occurs when the various physical and mechanical properties of aggregates are measured. According to BS 812 (1975) consistency of sample measurements within a laboratory (called *repeatability*) and between laboratories (called *reproducibility*) should be checked. Repeatability and reproducibility are investigated in Chapter 7.

Consider two infinite populations, A and B, each consisting of (for example) bulk density values, x_{Ai} and x_{Bi}, $i = 1, 2, 3, ...$, respectively, obtained from test samples of two lightweight aggregates. Population A has mean bulk density and standard deviation denoted by μ_A and σ_A, respectively, and those for population B are μ_B and σ_B, respectively.

Samples of sizes $n_A \geqslant 30$ and $n_B \geqslant 30$ are then taken (with or without replacement) from their respective populations and for each sample the mean bulk density is calculated, $\bar{x}_{Ai}$ and $\bar{x}_{Bi}$ (where subscript i denotes the ith sample). Now for each corresponding sample of bulk density values the difference in their mean bulk density, D_i, is determined, where $D_i = \bar{x}_{Ai} - \bar{x}_{Bi}$, $i = 1, 2, 3, ...$ Hence an infinite collection of sample mean differences is generated.

As with the variable $\bar{x}$ (sample mean) in Section 5.2, the variable D (sample mean difference) has a probability distribution, called **the distribution of sample mean differences**, which is approximately normal with mean μ_D and standard deviation σ_D given by

$$\mu_D = \mu_A - \mu_B \qquad [5.7]$$

and

$$\sigma_D = \sqrt{[(\sigma_{\bar{x}})^2_A + (\sigma_{\bar{x}})^2_B]} \qquad [5.8]$$

where, with the appropriate population subscript, $\sigma_{\bar{x}}$ is given by equation [5.3] (or equation [5.4] if the sampling is without replacement from a finite population).

Concerning the distribution of sample mean differences the following points are noted.

(a) Its approximation to a normal distribution improves as both n_A and n_B increase.
(b) Equations [5.7] and [5.8] are valid whatever the nature of the population distributions.
(c) If both population distributions are normal, then the distribution of sample mean differences is normal even when either n_A or n_B (or both) is less than 30.
(d) Equation [5.8] is valid provided the sample mean variables $\bar{x}_A$ and $\bar{x}_B$ ($D = \bar{x}_A - \bar{x}_B$) are independent of each other.

A normal distribution of sample mean differences is shown in Fig. 5.10, where properties (a)–(e) of Section 4.2 also apply in the D-variable.

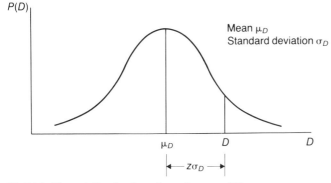

Fig 5.10 Normal distribution of sample mean differences

With reference to Section 5.1 the general sample property Q is now denoted by D so that for the distribution of sample mean differences equation [5.1] gives

$$z = \frac{D - \mu_D}{\sigma_D} \qquad [5.9]$$

where μ_D and σ_D are given by equations [5.7] and [5.8] respectively.

Example 5.4

15 bulk density values are required from test samples of an aggregate. A further 10 are required from test samples of a second aggregate. The mean bulk density and standard deviation of the first aggregate are known to be 1530 kg/m^3 and 5 kg/m^3, respectively, and those of the second aggregate are 1560 kg/m^3 and 8 kg/m^3, respectively. Find the probability that the mean of the bulk density values from the second aggregate will be more than 32 kg/m^3 greater than that from the first aggregate.

The population labelling is arbitrary and so may be performed in such a way that $\mu_D > 0$ (i.e. $\mu_A > \mu_B$). Hence to achieve this the population of bulk density values obtainable from the second aggregate is labelled A and that from the first aggregate is labelled B. Thus in this example the relevant data is

population A	population B
(second aggregate)	(first aggregate)
$\mu_A = 1560$ kg/m^3	$\mu_B = 1530$ kg/m^3
$\sigma_A = 8$ kg/m^3	$\sigma_B = 5$ kg/m^3
$n_A = 10$	$n_B = 15$

It is assumed that the population distributions of bulk density values are both normal so that, even though n_A, $n_B < 30$, the distribution of sample mean differences will be normal with

$$\mu_D = \mu_A - \mu_B = 30 \text{ kg/m}^3$$

and, since the sampling is from infinite populations without replacement

$$\sigma_D = \sqrt{[(\sigma_{\bar{x}})_A^2 + (\sigma_{\bar{x}})_B^2]}$$

$$= \sqrt{\left(\frac{\sigma_A^2}{n_A} + \frac{\sigma_B^2}{n_B}\right)}$$

$$= 2.84 \text{ kg/m}^3$$

The probability that $\bar{x}_A - \bar{x}_B > 32$ (i.e. $D > 32$) is required; this is represented by area A_1 in Fig. 5.11, i.e.

$$P(D > 32) = A_1 = 0.5 - A_2$$

Converting 32 to the z-variable:

$$z = \frac{D - \mu_D}{\sigma_D} = \frac{32 - 30}{2.84} = 0.70$$

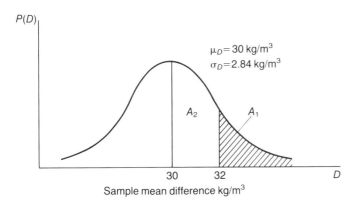

Fig 5.11 Normal distribution of sample mean differences

Thus area A_2 = 0.2580 and so

$P(D > 32)$ = 0.2420

Example 5.5

A building scientist obtains the moisture content in each of 30 test samples of a particular cement mix. A second scientist uses 40 test samples from the same mix. Given that the mix has a mean moisture content and standard deviation of 20% and 2%, respectively, find the probability that the mean moisture contents obtained by the two scientists differ by less than 0.2%.

In this example the population of moisture content measurements obtainable from the mix by the first scientist is the same as that for the second scientist. So, although there is really only one population, two identical populations are assumed; that associated with the first scientist is labelled *A* and that of the second is labelled *B*.

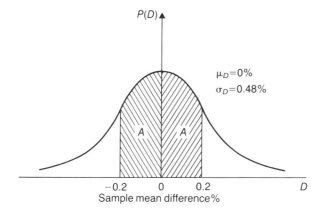

Fig 5.12 Normal distribution of sample mean differences

population A population B
(cement mix)   (the same mix)
$\mu_A = 20\%$ $\mu_B = 20\%$
$\sigma_A = 2\%$ $\sigma_B = 2\%$
$n_A = 30$ $n_B = 40$

As both samples are large the distribution of sample mean differences is considered normal with mean

$$\mu_D = \mu_A - \mu_B = 0\%$$

and, since the sampling is from infinite populations without replacement, the standard deviation is given by

$$\sigma_D = \sqrt{\left(\frac{\sigma_A^2}{n_A} + \frac{\sigma_B^2}{n_B} \right)}$$

$$= \sqrt{\left(\frac{2^2}{30} + \frac{2^2}{40} \right)}$$

$$= 0.48\%$$

The probability that the sample means $\bar{x}_A$ and $\bar{x}_B$ will differ by less than 0.2% is required, that is, the probability of $|\bar{x}_A - \bar{x}_B| < 0.2$ (i.e. $|D| < 0.2$) is required. With reference to Fig. 5.12,

$$P(|D| < 0.2) = P(-0.2 < D < 0.2)$$
$$= 2A$$

Converting 0.2 to the z-variable:

$$z = \frac{D - \mu_D}{\sigma_D} = \frac{0.2 - 0}{0.48} = 0.42$$

Hence area $A = 0.1628$ and so

$$P(|D| < 0.2) = 2 \times 0.1628$$
$$= 0.3256$$

Exercises

1. The masses of a large number of concrete cubes are normally distributed with mean 3 kg and standard deviation 0.12 kg. If 80 samples consisting of 36 cubes are considered, in how many samples is the mean mass

(a) between 3.01 kg and 3.03 kg
(b) less than 2.98 kg?
[(a) 19, (b) 13]

2. A builders merchant has a large number of lengths of copper pipe in store. The pipe lengths are normally distributed with mean length 2500 mm and standard deviation 10 mm. Given that the copper pipe is sold in batches of 4 dozen and over a period of time 300 batches are sold, find the number of batches that had mean length

(a) greater than 2502 mm
(b) less than 2497 mm.
[(a) 25, (b) 6]

3. Calculate the probability of failure of the CP 110 85% compliance criterion for grade C25 concrete with a standard deviation of 5 N/mm^2 and a 5% design failure.
[0.0084]

4. Calculate the probability of grade C15 concrete failing the CP 110 compliance criteria when it is designed for 3% of compressive strength results to fall below the characteristic strength. The standard deviation is 4 N/mm^2.
[0.0073, 0.0301]

5. A bricklayer takes 40 bricks from a stack with mean brick mass and standard deviation of 4 kg and 0.1 kg, respectively. He then takes 50 bricks from another stack with mean brick mass 4.5 kg and standard deviation 0.15 kg. Find the probability that the difference in the sample mean masses is more than 0.54 kg.
[0.0655]

6. Steel castings weigh on average 0.5 N with standard deviation 0.02 N. What is the probability that two batches of 1000 castings each will differ in mean weight by more than 0.001 N.
[0.2670]

Chapter 6

Statistical estimation

6.1 Introduction

The previous chapter explained how sampling can be used to obtain information about samples drawn from a population with *known* mean and standard deviation. However, unless specified, values for the population mean and standard deviation are usually unknown (because they are either impractical or impossible to calculate). Hence, in practice, the problem often becomes one of using samples to obtain information about the population. For example, information about the mean compressive strength of a concrete mix may be obtained from test cubes.

In this chapter sampling is used to obtain values of population properties, called **population parameters** (e.g. population mean and population mean difference), from the corresponding values of sample properties, called **sample statistics** (i.e. sample mean and sample mean difference, respectively). In other words, sample statistics will be used to *estimate* population parameters. The sample statistics are called **estimators** and their values are **estimates**.

6.2 Confidence intervals

In order for a sample statistic (e.g. the sample mean $\bar{x}$) to be usefully employed as an estimator of the corresponding population parameter (i.e. the population mean μ) it should be **unbiased** and **efficient**.

If a general sample statistic Q has a sampling distribution with mean μ_Q equal to the corresponding population parameter Ω, then the statistic is called an **unbiased estimator** of the parameter, otherwise it is called a biased estimator. The corresponding values of such statistics are known as unbiased or biased estimates, respectively.

Hence Q is an unbiased estimator of Ω if

$$\mu_Q = \Omega \qquad\qquad [6.1]$$

If Q is not unique, i.e. there are Q_i, $i = 1, 2, ...$, such that $\mu_{Q_i} = \Omega$, $i = 1, 2, ...$, then the particular Q_i whose sampling distribution has the smallest standard deviation is an **efficient estimator** of Ω, the other Q_i are inefficient estimators.

An estimate of a population parameter given by a single value is called a **point**

estimate of the parameter, whereas an estimate given by two values between which the parameter may be considered to lie is called an **interval estimate** of the parameter. For example, if the mean compressive strength of the concrete used on a project is estimated to be 34 N/mm², then this is a point estimate. However, an interval estimate for the mean compressive strength μ would be 34 ± 0.8 N/mm² (i.e. 33.2 < μ < 34.8). The ± 0.8 part of the interval estimate is called the **reliability** and represents a measure of the accuracy of the estimate. Because of this regard to accuracy interval estimates are preferable to point estimates.

The measure of accuracy incorporated in an interval estimate can be quantified in the following manner. Suppose the sampling distribution of sample statistic Q, obtained by drawing large samples (with or without replacement) from an infinite population, is normal with mean μ_Q and standard deviation σ_Q, as shown in Fig. 6.1. Now consider, for example, 95% of all values of Q to lie in the interval $Q_L < Q < Q_U$, hence $P(Q_L < Q < Q_U) = 0.95$. Thus the area under the normal curve between Q_L and Q_U is 0.95, i.e. $2A = 0.95$ so that $A = 0.475$. Hence the number of standard deviations Q_U is away from μ_Q is $z = z_c = 1.96$ (see Fig. 6.2), therefore $Q_U = \mu_Q + 1.96\ \sigma_Q$ and by symmetry

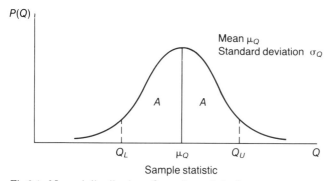

Fig 6.1 Normal distribution of sample statistic Q

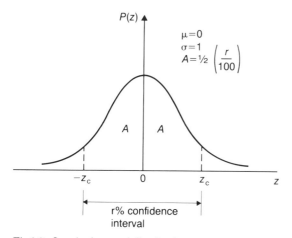

Fig 6.2 Standard normal distribution

65

$Q_L = \mu_Q - 1.96\ \sigma_Q$. Thus 95% of all values of Q lie in the interval

$$\mu_Q - 1.96\sigma_Q < Q < \mu_Q + 1.96\sigma_Q$$

which, for a particular value of Q, can be rearranged to give

$$Q - 1.96\sigma_Q < \mu_Q < Q + 1.96\sigma_Q$$

that is,

$$\mu_Q = Q \pm 1.96\sigma_Q \qquad\qquad [6.2]$$

Now if the sample statistic Q is an unbiased estimator of the corresponding population parameter Ω, then, using equation [6.1], equation [6.2] becomes

$$\Omega = Q \pm 1.96\sigma_Q \qquad\qquad [6.3]$$

which is the **95% confidence interval for** Ω. Alternatively, $Q \pm 1.96\sigma_Q$ is the interval estimate of Ω at the **95% confidence level**. In other words, it is possible to be 95% confident that the value of the population parameter Ω lies in the interval

$$Q - 1.96\sigma_Q < \Omega < Q + 1.96\sigma_Q$$

where $Q - 1.96\sigma_Q$ and $Q + 1.96\sigma_Q$ are called the **lower and upper 95% confidence limits,** respectively.

Equation [6.3] can be generalized to give the confidence interval for the population parameter Ω as

$$\Omega = Q \pm z_c\,\sigma_Q \qquad\qquad [6.4]$$

where the **confidence coefficient** z_c depends on the specified confidence level. With reference to Fig. 6.2, for a confidence level of $r\%$, area $A = \frac{1}{2}(r/100)$ and the associated value of z_c can be obtained using Table A.1 (in Appendix).

6.3   Confidence interval for the population mean

As stated in Section 5.2, for large samples the distribution of sample means is normally distributed with mean given by $\mu_{\bar{x}} = \mu$; that is, the mean of the sampling distribution for $\bar{x}$ (the sample mean) is equal to the population mean μ (i.e. the corresponding population parameter). Hence $\bar{x}$ can be used as an unbiased estimator of μ (it is also an efficient estimator).

If, in equation [6.4], Q, Ω and σ_Q are replaced by $\bar{x}$, μ and $\sigma_{\bar{x}}$, respectively, then the confidence interval for the population mean μ is

$$\mu = \bar{x} \pm z_c\,\sigma_{\bar{x}}$$

where $\sigma_{\bar{x}}$ is given by equation [5.3] (or equation [5.4] if the sampling is from a finite population). Thus, based on a large sample with mean $\bar{x}$, the confidence interval for μ is either

$$\mu = \bar{x} \pm z_c\frac{\sigma}{\sqrt{n}} \qquad\qquad [6.5]$$

for an infinite population, or, for a finite population of size n_P,

$$\mu = \bar{x} \pm z_c \frac{\sigma}{\sqrt{n}} \sqrt{\left(\frac{n_P - n}{n_P - 1}\right)} \qquad [6.6]$$

In both of the above equations the population standard deviation σ is required. However, as previously stated, its value is usually impractical (or impossible) to calculate. Therefore, in practice, σ is replaced in equations [6.5] and [6.6] by σ given by equation [1.6]. Hence equations [6.5] and [6.6] become, respectively,

$$\mu = \bar{x} \pm z_c \frac{\hat{\sigma}}{\sqrt{n}} \qquad [6.7]$$

and

$$\mu = \bar{x} \pm z_c \frac{\hat{\sigma}}{\sqrt{n}} \sqrt{\left(\frac{n_P - n}{n_P - 1}\right)} \qquad [6.8]$$

Note that equations [6.5] and [6.6] can be written respectively as

$$\mu = \bar{x} \pm z_c \sqrt{\frac{\sigma^2}{n}}$$

and

$$\mu = \bar{x} \pm z_c \sqrt{\left(\frac{\sigma^2}{n}\right)} \sqrt{\left(\frac{n_P - n}{n_P - 1}\right)}$$

where the square of the standard deviation, σ^2, is called the **variance**. Now an unbiased (and efficient) estimator of the variance is given by $\hat{\sigma}^2 = s^2 \, n/(n - 1)$, rather than by $\hat{\sigma}^2 = s^2$, where $n/(n - 1)$ is called **Bessel's correction factor**. This is why $\hat{\sigma} = s \sqrt{[n/(n - 1)]}$ is used rather than $\hat{\sigma} = s$ in equations [6.7] and [6.8], although the effect of Bessel's correction factor diminishes as n increases.

If the population distribution is normal and its standard deviation, σ, is known, then equations [6.5] and [6.6] are valid for $n < 30$.

Example 6.1

40 concrete cubes from a mix were tested for compressive strength and found to have mean strength 35 N/mm² and standard deviation 8 N/mm². Determine the 90% confidence interval for the mean compressive strength of the mix.
   Here the data given is

sample mean $\bar{x} = 35$ N/mm²
sample standard deviation $s = 8$ N/mm²
sample size $n = 40$

The population size is considered infinite and so the confidence interval for the population mean (i.e. mean strength of the mix) is given by

$$\mu = \bar{x} \pm z_c \, \frac{\hat{\sigma}}{\sqrt{n}}$$

where

$$\hat{\sigma} = s\sqrt{\left(\frac{n}{n-1}\right)} = 8 \times \sqrt{\left(\frac{40}{39}\right)}$$

$$= 8.1 \text{ N/mm}^2$$

This assumes that the value of s was not calculated using equation [1.4] with a denominator $n - 1$, as is sometimes the case in practice; if it was then $\hat{\sigma} = s = 8$ N/mm^2.

With reference to Fig. 6.2, for a 90% confidence interval area A is

$$A = \frac{1}{2}\left(\frac{90}{100}\right) = 0.45$$

and so $z_c = 1.64$. Hence the 90% confidence interval for the mean compressive strength of the mix is

$$\mu = 35 \pm 1.64 \times \frac{8.1}{\sqrt{40}}$$

that is,

$$\mu = 35 \pm 2.1$$

that is,

$$32.9 < \mu < 37.1 \text{ N/mm}^2$$

Example 6.2

From a store containing 150 masonry drill bits 30 were used and found to have a mean life of 15 hours with standard deviation 2 hours. Determine the 99% confidence limits for the mean life of all the bits in the store.

The relevant data is,

sample mean	$\bar{x}$	= 15 hours
sample standard deviation	s	= 2 hours
sample size	n	= 30
population size	n_P	= 150

Since the population size is finite the confidence limits for the population mean (i.e. mean life of the 150 bits) are given by

$$\bar{x} \pm z_c \, \frac{\hat{\sigma}}{\sqrt{n}} \, \sqrt{\left(\frac{n_P - n}{n_P - 1}\right)}$$

where (with s calculated using equation [1.4]),

$$\hat{\sigma} = s \sqrt{\left(\frac{n}{n-1}\right)} = 2 \times \sqrt{\frac{30}{29}}$$

$$= 2.0 \text{ hours}$$

Here the factor $[n/(n-1)]$ has no effect on s (correct to one decimal place). Because this is often the case some texts *automatically* write $\hat{\sigma} = s$ when $n \geqslant 30$.

For the 99% confidence limits area A in Fig. 6.2 is $\frac{1}{2}(99/100)$, i.e. $A = 0.495$. Thus $z_c = 2.58$ and so the 99% confidence limits for the mean life of the bits are

$$15 \pm 2.58 \times \frac{2}{\sqrt{30}} \times \sqrt{\left(\frac{150-30}{150-1}\right)}$$

that is,

$$15 \pm 0.8$$

that is,

14.2 hours and 15.8 hours.

6.4 Accuracy in building

An application of the use of statistical estimation in construction occurs in the assessment of building accuracy.

As explained in BS 5606 (1978), in any production process dimensional deviations are inevitable and so only by chance will the size of buildings or building components equal their specified target values.

The inevitable dimensional deviations are of the following two types.

(a) **Inherent deviations,** due to the nature of the materials used, for example
    (i) movement in foundations
    (ii) deflection of building elements under load
    (iii) deviations caused by thermal and moisture variations.
(b) **Induced deviations,** due to work done, for example,
    (i) setting out
    (ii) manufacture
    (iii) erection and assembly.

A statistical analysis of the results of a survey commissioned by the British Standards Institution (comprising sample measurements of buildings and building components from over 200 projects) revealed that a pattern of accuracy existed which was characteristic of each surveyed component and construction method. This regular pattern of accuracy is called the **characteristic accuracy** and can be represented graphically by a **characteristic accuracy curve** which is approximated by a normal distribution, as shown in Fig. 6.3. The characteristic accuracy curve for a particular component and construction method is defined by the mean size μ (called the **characteristic mean size**) and the standard deviation σ obtained from the survey results.

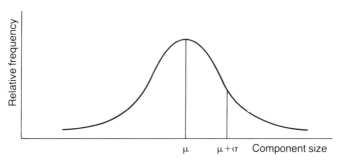

Fig 6.3 Characteristic accuracy curve for a particular building component and construction method

In BS 5606 characteristic accuracy is expressed in terms of the **displacement of the mean**, $\bar{x}_d$, and the standard deviation, where

$$\bar{x}_d = \text{(characteristic mean size)} - \text{(work size)} \qquad [6.9]$$

and the **work size** of a component is the size specified for manufacture to which the actual size should conform within specified permissible deviations, $\pm PD$, as shown in Fig. 6.4.

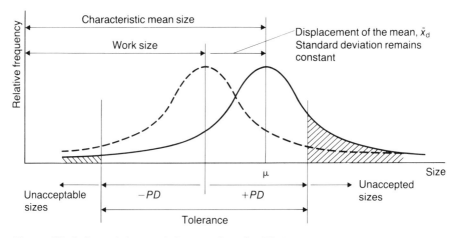

Fig 6.4 Work size and characteristic mean size; after BS 5606

The diagrams of Fig. 6.5 illustrate the effect of imposing specified permissible deviations on characteristic accuracy. In each diagram the characteristic accuracy of a particular component is represented by a normal distribution; furthermore, the displacement of the mean is taken to be $\bar{x}_d = \sigma$ (for example). By imposing permissible deviations of $\pm \sigma$, $\pm 2\sigma$ and $\pm 3\sigma$, successively, the diagrams show that the percentage of components with unacceptable sizes continually decreases. Hence $\pm 3\sigma$ are the preferred imposed permissible deviations because, compared to $\pm \sigma$ and $\pm 2\sigma$, the risk of component misfit is small.

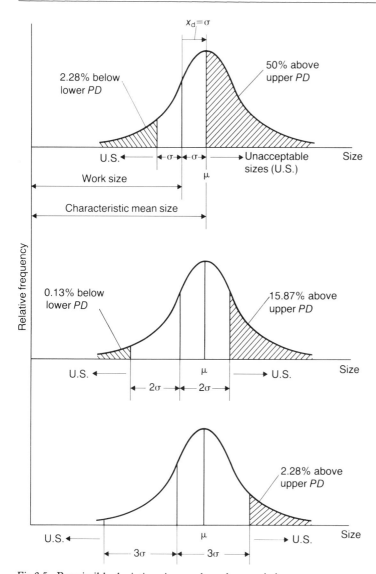

Fig 6.5   Permissible deviations imposed on characteristic accuracy

Example 6.3

To determine the height limits of a brick wall (less than 3 m high) of which the height dimension is critical from design considerations.

BS 5606 gives the deviation from the mean and standard deviation of the characteristic accuracy curve for a brick wall less than 3 m high as, respectively,

$$\bar{x}_d = 1.3 \text{ mm} \quad \text{and} \quad \sigma = 12.2 \text{ mm}$$

71

Since $\bar{x}_d$ = + 1.3 mm this means, by equation [6.9], that the characteristic mean size μ is greater than the specified work size H by 1.3 mm. This is illustrated in Fig. 6.6(a) in which the imposed permissible deviations are $\pm 3\sigma$.

With reference to Fig. 6.6(a), if x denotes wall height, then normal distribution property (e) (given to Section 4.2) gives

$$P(\mu - 3\sigma < x < \mu + 3\sigma) = 0.9974$$

that is,

$$P(-3\sigma < x - \mu < 3\sigma) \quad = 0.9974$$

thus

$$P(-(3\sigma + 2\bar{x}_d) < x - \mu < 3\sigma) > 0.9974$$

that is,

$$P(-(3\sigma + \bar{x}_d) < x - (\mu - \bar{x}_d) < 3\sigma + \bar{x}_d) > 0.9974$$

so, since $H = \mu - \bar{x}_d$,

$$P(-(3\sigma + \bar{x}_d) < x - H < 3\sigma + \bar{x}_d) > 0.9974$$

Hence, as shown in Fig. 6.6(b), the effect of imposing permissible deviations of $3\sigma + \bar{x}_d$ and $-(3\sigma + \bar{x}_d)$ is to reduce the risk of the wall height being unacceptably large or small, respectively. Thus $\pm (3\sigma + \bar{x}_d)$ represent the permissible deviations at the (at least) 99.74% confidence level. Therefore the (at least) 99.74% confidence limits for the wall height are $H \pm (3\sigma + \bar{x}_d)$.

As recognized by BS 5606, if good building practices are followed, then the risk that permissible deviations of $\pm (3\sigma + \bar{x}_d)$ will be exceeded is extremely small (at most 0.26%) because they embrace three standard deviations of random variation and the characteristic displacement of the mean.

For example, if H = 2800 mm, then the (at least) 99.74% confidence interval for the wall height is

$x = 2800 \pm ((3 \times 12.2) + 1.3)$
$\quad = 2800 \pm 37.9$

that is,

$2762.1 < x < 2837.9$ mm

(In BS 5606 the permissible deviations are rounded down to the nearest 5 mm; 37.9 mm would become 35 mm.)

6.5 Confidence interval for the population mean difference

As stated in Section 5.4, for large samples of sizes n_A and n_B taken from respective

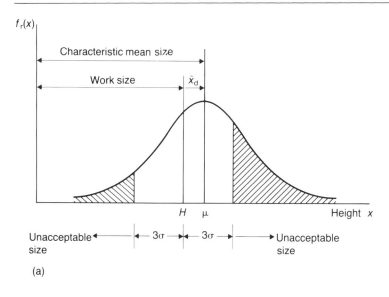

(a)

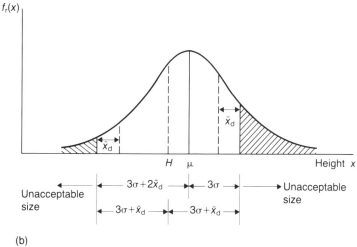

(b)

Fig 6.6 Characteristic accuracy curve for a brick wall (less than 3 m high)

populations A and B, the distribution of sample mean differences is normally distributed with mean equal to the population mean difference. Hence the sample statistic $\bar{x}_A - \bar{x}_B$ can be used as an unbiased estimator of $\mu_A - \mu_B$ (it is also an efficient estimator).

Now with Q, Ω and σ_Q replaced by $\bar{x}_A - \bar{x}_B$, $\mu_A - \mu_B$ and σ_D, respectively, equation [6.4] gives the confidence interval for the population mean difference $\mu_A - \mu_B$, based on the sample mean $\bar{x}_A - \bar{x}_B$, as

$$\mu_A - \mu_B = (\bar{x}_A - \bar{x}_B) \pm z_c\, \sigma_D \qquad [6.10]$$

73

An expression for the standard deviation of the distribution of sample mean differences, σ_D, is given by equation [5.8]. So equation [6.10] becomes

$$\mu_A - \mu_B = (\bar{x}_A - \bar{x}_B) \pm z_c \sqrt{[(\sigma_{\bar{x}})_A^2 + (\sigma_{\bar{x}})_B^2]} \qquad [6.11]$$

where, for infinite populations,

$$(\sigma_{\bar{x}})_A = \frac{\sigma_A}{\sqrt{n_A}} \qquad [6.12]$$

and, for finite populations of size $(n_P)_A$,

$$(\sigma_{\bar{x}})_A = \frac{\sigma_A}{\sqrt{n_A}} \sqrt{\left(\frac{(n_P)_A - n_A}{(n_P)_A - 1}\right)} \qquad [6.13]$$

Similarly for $(\sigma_{\bar{x}})_B$. As with the confidence interval for the population mean (see Section 6.3 of this chapter), the unknown population standard deviation σ_A is, in practice, replaced in equations [6.12] and [6.13] by $\hat{\sigma}_A$. Similarly for σ_B.

If both population distributions are normal and both their standard deviations, σ_A and σ_B, are known, then equation [6.11] (with equations [6.12] and [6.13]) is valid when n_A or n_B (or both) is less than 30.

Example 6.4

Two manufacturers, X and Y, produce wire for use in prestressed concrete. Given that 45 test lengths from manufacturer X had mean breaking strength (stress) 2400 N/mm² and standard deviation 55 N/mm², and 35 test lengths from manufacturer Y had mean breaking strength 2500 N/mm² and standard deviation 50 N/mm², calculate a point and interval estimate for the difference in the mean breaking strength of the wire produced by the two manufacturers, at the 95% confidence level.

Since the labelling of the populations in equation [6.11] is arbitrary it may be performed in such a way that $\bar{x}_A - \bar{x}_B > 0$. Hence, for the two populations of breaking strength values in this example, the labelling will be $A \leftrightarrow Y$ and $B \leftrightarrow X$.

Manufacturer X Manufacturer Y
$\bar{x}_X = 2400$ N/mm² $\bar{x}_Y = 2500$ N/mm²
$s_X = 55$ N/mm² $s_Y = 50$ N/mm²
$n_X = 45$ $n_Y = 35$

A point estimate (which is independent of confidence level) of the population mean difference is given by

$$\bar{x}_Y - \bar{x}_X = 2500 - 2400$$
$$= 100 \text{ N/mm}^2$$

Both populations of breaking strength values are considered to be infinite so that the interval estimate of the population mean difference is, using equations [6.11] and [6.12],

$$\mu_Y - \mu_X = (\bar{x}_Y - \bar{x}_X) \pm z_c \sqrt{\left(\frac{\hat{\sigma}_Y^2}{n_Y} + \frac{\hat{\sigma}_X^2}{n_X} \right)}$$

where (with s_X and s_Y calculated using equation [1.4])

$$\hat{\sigma}_X^2 = s_X^2 \left(\frac{n_X}{n_X - 1} \right) = (55)^2 \times \frac{45}{44}$$

$$= 3093.8 \text{ N/mm}^2$$

and

$$\hat{\sigma}_Y^2 = s_Y^2 \left(\frac{n_Y}{n_Y - 1} \right) = (50)^2 \times \frac{35}{34}$$

$$= 2573.5 \text{ N/mm}^2$$

With reference to Fig. 6.2, at the 95% confidence level area $A = \frac{1}{2}(95/100) = 0.475$. Thus $z_c = 1.96$ and so the interval estimate for the difference in the mean breaking strength of the wire produced by the two manufacturers is, at the 95% confidence level,

$$\mu_Y - \mu_X = 100 \pm 1.96 \times \sqrt{\left(\frac{2573.5}{35} + \frac{3093.8}{45} \right)}$$

$$= 100 \pm 23.4$$

that is,

$$76.6 < \mu_Y - \mu_X < 123.4 \text{ N/mm}^2$$

6.6 Building design

The use of statistical estimation in the assessment of building accuracy has been explained in Section 6.4; here an application in the related area of building design is discussed.

In DD 22 (1972) an attempt is made to represent accurately the complex inter-actions between the dimensional deviations of components in a building. In this attempt a common basis for the sizing of building components is used. Its purpose is, through the use of standard unmodified components (i.e. *modular* building components), to limit the variety of different sizes while maintaining dimensional and planning flexibility for the building designer.

One of the main aims of DD 22 is to provide building designers with a method of calculating the maximum and minimum joint clearances between components used in particular assembly situations. To achieve this aim DD 22 uses the concept of **dimensional co-ordination** in which building components are given a dual description; a **co-ordinating size** and a work size. The co-ordinating size is the size of the spatial

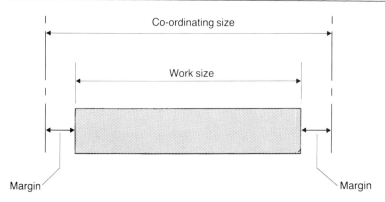

Fig 6.7 Co-ordinating size and work size (for length dimension only); after DD 22

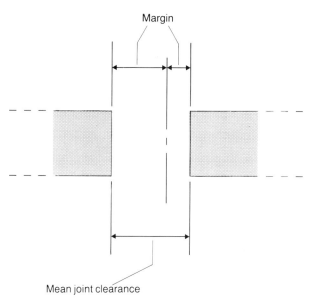

Fig 6.8 Margin and mean joint clearance; after DD 22

envelope containing the component (see Fig. 6.7) and forms the basis on which components are organized in the planning of dimensionally co-ordinated buildings.

With reference to Fig. 6.8 the distance between the nearest surface of the component (its joint face) and the co-ordinating plane is known as the **margin**; this provides an allowance for dimensional deviations (i.e. induced and inherent deviations, see Section 6.4). With joined components the sum of the margins is called the **mean joint clearance**.

For induced deviations the range of probable joint clearance from the mean can be expressed in terms of the **clearance variability**. That is, the variation from the mean joint clearance due to a particular cause of induced deviation is assumed to be described

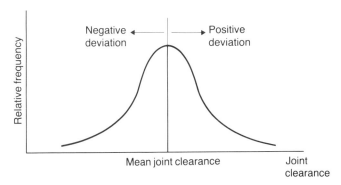

Fig 6.9 Clearance variability curve for a particular cause of induced deviation; after DD 22

by a **clearance variability curve** that approximates a normal distribution (as shown in Fig. 6.9). Hence statistical methods can be used to assess the chance of joint misfit.

Since the variation in joint clearance due to each cause of induced deviation is assumed to be normally distributed, the combined effect of all induced deviations will result in a normal joint-clearance variability curve with standard deviation given by

$$\sigma = \sqrt{(\sigma_1^2 + \sigma_2^2 + \dots + \sigma_n^2)}$$

where σ_i, $i = 1, 2, \dots, n$, denote the standard deviations of the clearance variability curves associated with n individual causes of induced deviation.

Unlike induced deviations, inherent deviations (due, for example, to thermal and moisture variations) are calculable to a reasonable degree of accuracy for particular circumstances. Hence there is no consideration of probability in assessing the effect of inherent deviations on joint clearances.

Exercises

1. A large consignment of lengths of timber (of the same standard type) is delivered to a building site. Given that a sample of 60 lengths had mean length 5000 mm and standard deviation 10 mm, calculate the 95% and 99% confidence limits for the mean length of the timber in the consignment.
[5000 ± 2.55 mm, 5000 ± 3.35 mm]

2. Over a period of time concrete cubes from on-site mixes were tested and found to have mean compressive strength 34 N/mm^2 and standard deviation 3 N/mm^2. Calculate an interval estimate for the mean strength of all concrete used on site at the 80% and 90% confidence levels.
[33.45 $< \mu <$ 34.55 N/mm^2, 33.30 $< \mu <$ 34.70 N/mm^2]

3. Use BS 5606 to determine the thickness limits for a brick wall if the intended thickness (i.e. work size) is 480 mm.
[480 ± 28.1 mm]

4. Use BS 5606 to determine the length limits for a timber panel if the work size is 3000 mm.

[3000 ± 6.1 mm]

5. Two randomly selected groups of 50 operatives from two national construction companies are timed to perform a certain operation. The first group take a mean time of 112 min and standard deviation 12 min. The second group take a mean time of 117 min and standard deviation 9 min. Find the 95% confidence interval for the difference in the mean times taken to perform the operation by all operatives from the two companies.

[$0.8 < \mu_D < 9.2$ min]

6. Over a period of time, on two building sites, concrete cubes were tested for compressive strength. Given that 100 cubes from the first site had mean strength 35 N/mm^2 and standard deviation 6 N/mm^2, and 75 cubes from the second site had mean strength 37 N/mm^2 and standard deviation 5 N/mm^2, calculate an interval estimate for the difference in the mean strength of the concrete used on the two sites at the 90% confidence level.

[$0.63 < \mu_D < 3.37$ N/mm^2]

Chapter 7

Statistical decisions

7.1 Introduction

As shown in the previous two chapters, sampling is used when it is impractical (or impossible) to measure the required property of each item comprising a population. In this chapter sampling is performed with the aim of making a decision about a population based on sample data. For example, the compressive strengths of test concrete cubes can be used to decide whether or not the designed target mean strength of a mix is achieved.

Statistical decisions made about a population on the basis of sample data usually involve statements of the decision and a specified measure of the accuracy of the decision. In this chapter the sample sizes will be large (i.e. $n \geqslant 30$) and the statistical method employed to reach a decision is called a **hypothesis test** (or **significance test**).

7.2 Hypothesis tests

(a) The null and alternative hypothesis

In order to make a decision about a population assumptions are made about it. These assumptions are called **hypotheses**.

Usually a hypothesis is formulated with the purpose of rejecting (or nullifying) it, such a hypothesis is called the **null hypothesis** and is denoted by H_0. A hypothesis which differs from the null hypothesis (that is, it is an alternative option) is called the **alternative hypothesis** and is denoted by H_1.

In formulating the null and alternative hypotheses appropriate to a particular decision the following comments should be noted. The null hypothesis is a statement that the specified (or assumed) original situation is unchanged, that is, the status quo prevails. In contrast the alternative hypothesis is a statement that represents what is suspected (or required to be shown) about the current situation.

For example, suppose the designed target mean strength of a mix is 35 N/mm^2 and a sample of test cubes has mean compressive strength 33.5 N/mm^2. The decision may be to decide whether or not the target mean strength is achieved. So here

Null hypothesis   : target mean strength is achieved (the status quo)
Alternative hypothesis : target mean strength is not achieved (to be shown)

or, in terms of symbols,

H_0: $\mu = 35 \text{ N/mm}^2$
H_1: $\mu \neq 35 \text{ N/mm}^2$,

where μ denotes the actual mean strength of the mix (i.e. the population mean) and 35 N/mm^2 is the specified mean strength of the mix.

With reference to the alternative hypothesis particular attention must be given to the *wording* of the decision. For instance, if the decision is to decide whether or not the mean strength of the mix is less than designed value, then

H_0: $\mu = 35 \text{ N/mm}^2$
H_1: $\mu < 35 \text{ N/mm}^2$.

Similarly, if the test cubes have mean strength 36 N/mm^2 and it is required to decide whether or not the mean strength of the mix is greater than the designed value, then

H_0: $\mu = 35 \text{ N/mm}^2$
H_1: $\mu > 35 \text{ N/mm}^2$.

Hence, in general, with a null hypothesis of $\mu = 35 \text{ N/mm}^2$ there are *three* possibilities of an alternative hypothesis,

$$\mu \overset{>}{\underset{<}{\neq}} 35 \text{ N/mm}^2.$$

and which mathematical symbol is chosen depends on the wording of the decision to be made.

(b) Test statistics

The null and alternative hypotheses are just two elements of a hypothesis test. A third element is the **test statistic**.

A test statistic is an expression whose value is calculated using sample data. Different sampling distributions have different test statistics. For the normal distributions of sample means and sample mean differences the test statistic is the standard normal variable z and is given by, respectively,

$$z = \frac{\bar{x} - \mu_{\bar{x}}}{\sigma_{\bar{x}}} \qquad\qquad [7.1]$$

(see equation [5.5])

and

$$z = \frac{D - \mu_D}{\sigma_D} \qquad\qquad [7.2]$$

(see equation [5.9]).

(c) The rejection region

The final element of a hypothesis test is the **rejection region**. For a normal sampling distribution with test statistic given by the standard normal variable z, the rejection region is an interval ($z > z_a$ in Fig. 7.1(a), or $z < z_a$ in Fig. 7.1(b)) or, in some instances, two intervals (both $z > z_a$ and $z < -z_a$ in Fig. 7.1(c)) on the z-axis under the standard normal distribution curve.

If the calculated value of z given by equation [7.1] or equation [7.2] lies in the rejection region, then H_0 is rejected and so H_1 is accepted, if it doesn't then H_0 is accepted and H_1 is rejected.

The rejection regions shown in Fig. 7.1(a) and Fig. 7.1(b) are associated with alternative hypotheses involving '>' and '<', respectively, and the corresponding hypothesis tests are called **one-tailed hypothesis tests** (or **one-tailed tests**). The rejection region shown in Fig. 7.1(c) is associated with an H_1 involving '$\neq$' and results in a **two-tailed hypothesis test** (or **two-tailed test**).

How the boundary value z_a (sometimes called the **critical value of z**) is obtained is now explained.

(d) Level of significance

When a decision about a population is based purely on sample information it is not possible to be 100% sure that the decision made is correct. For example, the null hypothesis could be rejected when it should be accepted; this is called a **Type I error**. Alternatively, a **Type II error** is made when the null hypothesis is accepted when it should be rejected. Hence when making statistical decisions there is always the possibility that a Type I error (for example) will be made. However it is possible to specify the maximum acceptable probability for this to occur.

When making a statistical decision, the **level of significance**, denoted by α, specifies the *maximum* probability for which a Type I error is tolerated. (In this context α can be considered as a measure of the accuracy of the decision.) A common level of significance is $\alpha = 0.05$ (or 5%), that is, the probability of rejecting H_0 when it should be accepted is specified to be at most 0.05.

With reference to Fig. 7.1, the level of significance is represented graphically by the total area which is under the curve and above the rejection region. Thus in Fig. 7.1(a) and (b) area $a = \alpha$, and in Fig. 7.1(c) $a = \alpha/2$.

Now if, for example, $\alpha = 0.05$, then in Fig. 7.1(a) and (b) (which are associated with one-tailed hypothesis tests) area $a = 0.05$. Thus area $A = 0.45$ and so, using Table A.1 in the Appendix, $z_a = z_{0.05} = 1.64$ in Fig. 7.1(a) and -1.64 in Fig. 7.1(b). For a two-tailed hypothesis test, see Fig. 7.1(c), area $a = 0.025$ so that area $A = 0.475$ and $z_a = z_{0.025} = 1.96$.

Hence if the calculated value of the test statistic z, given by equation [7.1] or equation [7.2] is such that $z > 1.64$ in Fig. 7.1(a) or $z < -1.64$ in Fig. 7.1(b) (or $-1.96 > z > 1.96$ in Fig. 7.1(c)), then the decision would be *to reject the null hypothesis and accept the alternative hypothesis at the 0.05 level of significance*. Note that although the null hypothesis is rejected the probability of making the wrong decision (i.e. making a Type I error) is acknowledged and specified to be at most $\alpha = 0.05$.

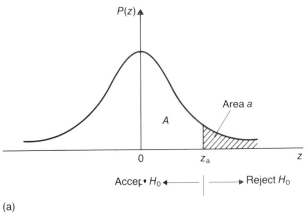

(a)

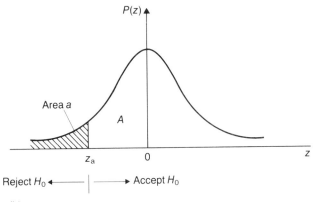

(b)

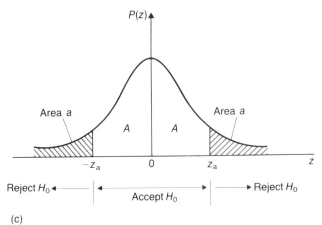

(c)

Fig 7.1 Rejection regions

If the above inequalities were all reversed, then the null hypothesis would be accepted and the alternative hypothesis rejected at the 0.05 significance level.

Example 7.1

A certain concrete mix is designed to have a mean compressive strength of 45 N/mm². A sample of 40 test cubes was found to have mean strength 42 N/mm² and standard deviation 6 N/mm². Decide, at the 1% level of significance, whether or not the mix is of inferior quality with respect to compressive strength.

The null and alternative hypotheses are, respectively,

H_0: $\mu = 45$ N/mm²   (status quo)
H_1: $\mu < 45$ N/mm²   (to be shown)

where μ denotes the mean compressive strength of the mix.

The alternative hypothesis indicates that a one-tailed test is appropriate with the rejection region in the negative tail of the standard normal distribution (see Fig. 7.1(b)).

Test statistic: for the normal distribution of sample means (see equation [7.1]),

$$z = \frac{\bar{x} - \mu_{\bar{x}}}{\sigma_{\bar{x}}}$$

Hence, under H_0 (i.e. $\mu = 45$ N/mm²)

$$\mu_{\bar{x}} = \mu = 45 \text{ N/mm}^2$$

and, with sampling from an infinite population (the mix), $\sigma_{\bar{x}} = \sigma/\sqrt{n}$. However, since σ is unknown, it is estimated by $\hat{\sigma} = s\sqrt{[n/(n-1)]}$. Thus

$$\sigma_{\bar{x}} = \frac{s}{\sqrt{(n-1)}} = \frac{6}{\sqrt{39}} = 0.96 \text{ N/mm}^2.$$

Now with sample mean $\bar{x} = 42$ N/mm² the value of the test statistic is

$$z = \frac{42 - 45}{0.96} = -3.13$$

Rejection region: one-tailed test with $\alpha = 0.01$. With reference to Fig. 7.1(b), area $a = \alpha = 0.01$ and so area $A = 0.49$. Thus $z_{0.01} = -2.33$.

Since $-3.13 < z_{0.01}$ the value of the test statistic lies in the rejection region. Therefore H_0 is rejected and H_1 is accepted, that is, at the 1% significance level, the mix is of inferior quality (with respect to compressive strength).

Example 7.2

Two rival manufacturers, A and B, produce steel rods for use in reinforced concrete. An independent investigation found that 40 test lengths from manufacturer A had mean yield strength 4.4 kN and standard deviation 0.5 kN, and 50 test lengths from manufacturer B had mean yield strength 4.6 kN and standard deviation 0.6 kN. Decide, at the 5% significance level, whether or not there is any difference in the quality of the rods (with respect to yield strength) produced by the rival manufacturers.

The null and alternative hypotheses are, respectively,

$H_0: \mu_A = \mu_B$ (status quo)
$H_1: \mu_A \neq \mu_B$ (to be shown)

where μ_A denotes the mean yield strength of all rods produced by manufacturer A. Similarly for μ_B.

Inspection of the alternative hypothesis reveals that a two-tailed test is appropriate with the rejection region in both tails of the standard normal distribution (see Fig. 7.1(c)).

Test statistic: for the normal distribution of sample mean differences (see equation [7.2])

$$z = \frac{D - \mu_D}{\sigma_D}$$

Hence, under H_0 (i.e. $\mu_A = \mu_B$)

$$\mu_D = \mu_A - \mu_B = 0\,\text{kN}$$

and, with sampling from infinite populations,

$$\sigma_D = \sqrt{\left(\frac{\sigma_A^2}{n_A} + \frac{\sigma_B^2}{n_B}\right)}$$

The unknown population standard deviations, σ_A and σ_B, can be replaced by their estimators, $\hat{\sigma}_A$ and $\hat{\sigma}_B$ respectively, so that

$$\sigma_D = \sqrt{\left(\frac{s_A^2}{n_A - 1} + \frac{s_B^2}{n_B - 1}\right)}$$

i.e.

$$= \sqrt{\left(\frac{(0.5)^2}{39} + \frac{(0.6)^2}{49}\right)} = 0.12\,\text{kN}$$

The sample mean difference D is such that

$$D = \bar{x}_A - \bar{x}_B = 4.4 - 4.6 = -0.2\,\text{kN}$$

and so the value of the test statistic is

$$z = \frac{-0.2 - 0}{0.12} = -1.67$$

Rejection region: two-tailed test with $\alpha = 0.05$. With reference to Fig. 7.1(c) area $a = \alpha/2 = 0.025$ and so area $A = 0.475$. Thus $z_{0.025} = 1.96$.

Since $-z_{0.025} < -1.67 < z_{0.025}$ the value of the test statistic does not lie in the rejection region. Therefore H_0 is accepted and H_1 is rejected, that is, at the 5% significance level, there is no difference in the quality of steel rods produced by the two manufacturers.

7.3 Acceptance sampling

In any production process the product is usually supplied to the consumer (or customer) in a batch, or lot. The following question then arises: how is the consumer to decide whether or not a particular batch is of an acceptable standard, bearing in mind that 100% inspection is usually not possible (because of the time, effort or cost involved, or the use of a destructive test).

Because each individual item comprising the batch is not inspected the decision as to the acceptability of the product is based on a sample taken from the batch, a process called **acceptance sampling**.

For example, in acceptance sampling, the proportion p of defectives in a batch can be used to describe the quality of the batch. If the consumer agrees that a small proportion, p_0, of defective items in a batch is permissible, then the ideal **sampling scheme** (or **decision rule**) would be one such that;

(a) all batches in which $p \leqslant p_0$ are accepted (this is fair to the producer)
(b) all batches in which $p > p_0$ are rejected (this is fair to the consumer).

If $P_a(p)$ denotes the probability of accepting a batch in which the actual proportion of defectives is p, then the ideal sampling scheme can be stated as

$$P_a(p) = 1 \quad \text{for } p \leqslant p_0$$
$$P_a(p) = 0 \quad \text{for } p > p_0$$

The graph of $P_a(p)$ against p is shown in Fig. 7.2 and represents the **operating characteristic curve** (**OC curve**) for this sampling scheme.

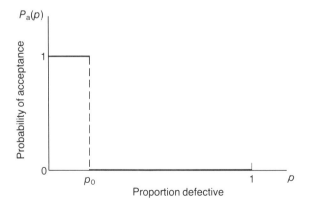

Fig 7.2 Ideal operating-characteristic curve

Unfortunately the ideal OC curve as shown in Fig. 7.2 is only possible with 100% inspection of the batch. In practice, as only a sample from the batch is inspected, there is always the possibility of good quality batches being rejected when they should be accepted and poor quality batches being accepted when they should be rejected (i.e. Type I and Type II errors, respectively).

As only 100% inspection will always guarantee perfect assessment of the quality of a batch, the most that can be expected of a sampling scheme is that the probability of acceptance should be *high* for batches of *good* quality and *low* for batches of *poor* quality. This would mean the OC curve being as near as possible to the ideal (see Fig. 7.2) within the limitations of the amount of inspection it is possible to carry out.

For a particular sampling scheme the probability of batch acceptance can be calculated so that both the producer and consumer know what risks they are taking. As an example consider a sample of 10 items taken from a batch and the sampling scheme; accept the batch if there is no more than 1 defective item, otherwise reject it.

It is assumed that the batch size is large relative to the sample size so that for each sample item selected at random without replacement the probability of being defective is the constant value p (i.e. the proportion defective). Hence the binomial distribution can be used to determine the probability of obtaining x defectives in a sample of 10 items, see equation [3.1]:

$$P(x) = {}_{10}C_x p^x (1 - p)^{10-x} \qquad [7.3]$$

Now the probability of accepting the batch, that is, the probability of obtaining at most 1 defective item in a sample of 10 items, is given by (using equation [7.3]),

$$\begin{aligned}P_a(p) &= P(0) + P(1) \\ &= (1 - p)^{10} + 10p(1 - p)^9 \\ &= (1 + 9p)(1 - p)^9 \qquad [7.4]\end{aligned}$$

In equation [7.4] $P_a(p)$ can be evaluated for various values of p, $0 \leqslant p \leqslant 1$, and the results displayed graphically by means of the OC curve for this sampling scheme, as shown in Fig. 7.3.

Notice that the OC curve (and therefore the sampling scheme) can be defined by two parameters; the sample size n (here $n = 10$) and the maximum allowable number of defectives, c, where c is called the **acceptance number** (here $c = 1$).

If the consumer agrees that a proportion of defectives in the batch of no more than $p = p_0$ is permissible (i.e. $0 \leqslant p \leqslant p_0$), then Fig. 7.3 shows that the least probability of acceptance is $P_a(p) = 1 - \alpha$. Ideally, for $p \leqslant p_0$, $P_a(p) = 1$ (i.e. the batch should be accepted, see Fig. 7.2) and so α, called the **producer's risk**, gives the *maximum* probability of rejecting a good quality batch when it should be accepted. For $p > p_0$ the ideal OC curve shown in Fig. 7.2 gives $P_a(p) = 0$ (i.e. the batch should be rejected). However, for $p > p_0$ in Fig. 7.3, $P_a(p) = \beta$, the probability of accepting a poor quality batch when it should be rejected. The quantity β is called the **consumer's risk**.

To satisfy both the producer and consumer the values of n and c must be chosen so that the producer's and consumer's risks are acceptably low to both parties. This can be achieved, as illustrated in Fig. 7.4, by specifying the value of α at p_0 (where p_0 is called the **acceptable quality level**, AQL) and the value of β at p_1 (where p_1 is called

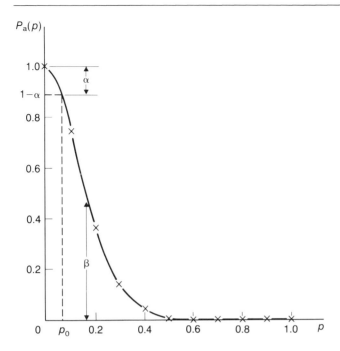

Fig 7.3 Operating-characteristic curve

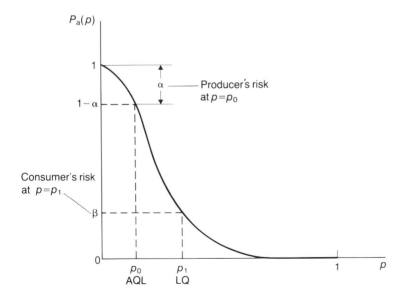

Fig 7.4 Acceptable quality level, *AQL*, and limiting quality, *LQ*

the **limiting quality**, LQ, or if expressed as a percentage, $100p_1\ \%$, the **lot tolerance percentage defective**, $LTPD$). In this manner the producer will know that for a batch in which $p \leqslant p_0$ the maximum probability it is rejected when it should be accepted is α. Also the consumer will know that for a batch in which $p \geqslant p_1$ the maximum probability it is accepted when it should be rejected is β.

The acceptance sampling considered so far simply classified the sampled items as either 'acceptable' or 'defective'; it is known as *acceptance sampling by attributes* and is used with discrete random variables. With some items a particular property can be measured so that with continuous random variables *acceptance sampling by variables* is used (see Example 7.4 and Section 7.4).

As previously stated the consumer's risk, β, is the probability that a poor quality batch is accepted when it should be rejected, that is, the probability of making a Type II error with hypotheses,

$$H_0: p = p_0$$
$$H_1: p > p_0 \tag{7.5}$$

In other words an OC curve can be considered as a graphical representation of the probability of making a Type II error under particular hypotheses.

The producer's risk, α, is the maximum probability of rejecting a good quality batch when it should be accepted, that is, the probability of making a Type I error with hypotheses [7.5]. Hence the producer's risk corresponds to the level of significance of a hypothesis test.

Example 7.3

Large consignments of roof tiles are delivered to a building site.

(a) Construct an OC curve for the acceptability of a consignment if, when 15 tiles are inspected, the acceptance scheme is,
  (i) accept the consignment if no more than 2 tiles are damaged
  (ii) otherwise reject the consignment.
(b) Determine the producer's risk if the percentage of damaged tiles (due to handling and transportation) is 10% per consignment.

(a) Assuming the binomial distribution applies, the probability of obtaining x damaged tiles in a sample of 15 is given by

$$P(x) = {}_{15}C_x p^x (1 - p)^{15-x}$$

where p is the proportion of damaged tiles in a consignment.

With reference to the acceptance scheme, the probability of accepting a consignment, $P_a(p)$, is given by

$$P_a(p) = P(0) + P(1) + P(2)$$
$$= (1 - p)^{15} + 15p(1 - p)^{14} + 105p^2(1 - p)^{13}$$
$$= (1 + 13p + 91p^2)(1 - p)^{13}$$

The required OC curve defined by the above equation is presented in Fig. 7.5.

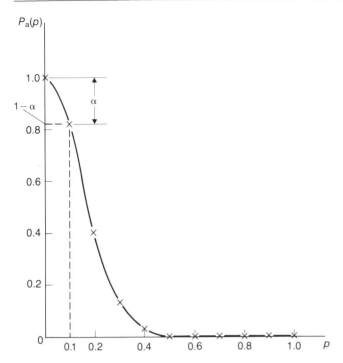

Fig 7.5 Operating characteristic curve

(b)   The percentage of damaged tiles in a consignment is 10% so that $p = 0.1$. Hence the producer's risk, α, can either be obtained approximately from the *OC* curve or calculated as follows:

$$\alpha = 1 - P_a (0.1)$$
$$= 1 - 0.8159 = 0.1841$$

Example 7.4

A certain type of heavy duty chain (for use on construction projects) has, according to the manufacturer, a mean breaking strength of 8 kN and standard deviation 0.5 kN. A new production process is developed which, it is thought, will increase the breaking strength of the chains. To investigate this a sample of 64 chains produced by the new process is tested.

Construct an OC curve associated with the breaking strength of the (new process) chains assuming the standard deviation remains at 0.5 kN.

In terms of a hypothesis test the null and alternative hypotheses associated with this example are

$$H_0 : \mu = 8 \text{ kN}$$
$$H_1 : \mu > 8 \text{ kN}$$

where μ denotes the mean breaking strength of all the new process chains produced by the manufacturer. The alternative hypothesis indicates that a one-tailed test is appropriate with rejection region in the positive tail of the standard normal distribution (see Fig. 7.1(a)).

Test statistic: for the normal distribution of sample mean breaking strength the test statistic is

$$z = \frac{\bar{x} - \mu}{\sigma/\sqrt{n}}$$

where

population mean	μ	$= 8 \text{ kN (under } H_0)$
population standard deviation	σ	$= 0.5 \text{ kN}$
sample size	n	$= 64$

Rejection region: one-tailed test and consider the significance level to be $\alpha = 0.01$.

With reference to Fig. 7.1(a), area $a = \alpha = 0.01$ and area $A = 0.5 - a = 0.49$, so that $z_a = z_{0.01} = 2.33$. Hence if $z > 2.33$ the null hypothesis is rejected and the alternative hypothesis is accepted. To determine the value of the sample mean corresponding to $z_{0.01}$, i.e. $\bar{x}_{0.01}$, the test statistic can be rearranged to give

$$\bar{x}_{0.01} = \mu + z_{0.01} \frac{\sigma}{\sqrt{n}}$$

$$= 8 + 2.33 \times \frac{0.5}{8} = 8.15 \text{ kN}$$

Thus if $\bar{x} > 8.15$, then H_0 is rejected and H_1 is accepted at the 0.01 significance level, that is, the probability of making a Type I error is 0.01. Furthermore, with reference to Fig. 7.6, the probability of making a Type II error, β, is given by

$\beta = 0.5 + A$
$= 0.5 + 0.49 = 0.99$

The probability of making a Type II error (i.e. accepting H_0 when it should be rejected) is now calculated for various possible values of the actual mean breaking strength of the new process chains.

For instance, if $\mu = 8.1 \text{ kN}$ in Fig. 7.6, then the test statistic gives

$$z = \frac{8.15 - 8.1}{0.5/8} = 0.8$$

Hence area $A = 0.2881$ so that $\beta = 0.7881$. Similar calculations can be performed with, for example, $\mu = 7.9 \ (0.05) \ 8.4 \text{ kN}$. The resulting OC curve is shown in Fig. 7.7 (if $\mu > \bar{x}_{0.01}$ then $\beta = 0.5 - A$).

As the OC curve shows, if the mean breaking strength of the new process chains is in fact 8.2 kN (for example), then, based on a test sample of size 64 and $\alpha = 0.01$, the probability of accepting the old value of 8 kN is $\beta = 0.21$.

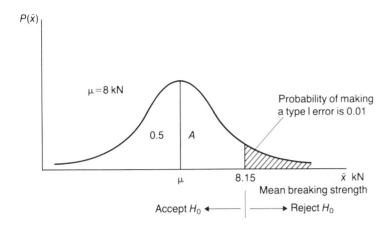

Fig 7.6 Normal distribution of sample mean breaking strength

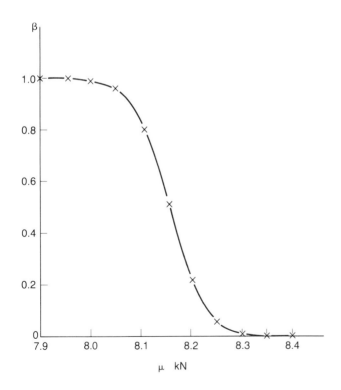

Fig 7.7 Operating characteristic curve

7.4 Operating characteristic curve for concrete

As stated in Section 5.3, the CP 110 (1972) mean-of-four compliance criterion is

$$\bar{x}_{min} = \text{(characteristic strength)} + 0.5 \times \text{(current margin)} \qquad [7.6]$$

where $\bar{x}_{min}$ denotes the minimum permissible mean compressive strength of four consecutive test cubes. At the 5% defective level the characteristic strength, k, and the current margin, 1.64σ, are shown in Fig. 7.8. Equation [7.6] can then be written as

$$\bar{x}_{min} = k + 0.5 \times (1.64\sigma)$$

that is

$$\bar{x}_{min} = k + 0.82\sigma \qquad [7.7]$$

However, if the quality of the concrete production deteriorates, by a shift of the mean strength μ towards the characteristic strength, the standard deviation σ remaining constant, then, at the $m\%$ defective level (where $m > 5$) the current margin will now be $|z|\sigma$ (where $|z| < 1.64$) as shown in Fig. 7.9.

Hence, at the $m\%$ defective level, it is seen in Fig. 7.9 that $k = \mu - |z|\sigma$, which when substituted into equation [7.7] gives

$$\bar{x}_{min} = (\mu - |z|\sigma) + 0.82\sigma$$

that is

$$\bar{x}_{min} = \mu + (0.82 - |z|)\sigma \qquad [7.8]$$

For sampling without replacement (a destructive test is used on concrete cubes) from an 'infinite' population (the mix) the distribution of sample mean compressive strengths, as shown in Fig. 7.10, has mean and standard deviation given by $\mu_{\bar{x}} = \mu$ and $\sigma_{\bar{x}} = \sigma/\sqrt{n}$, respectively (see Section 5.2). Here the sample size $n = 4$, so that in Fig. 7.10,

$$\mu_{\bar{x}} = \mu \qquad [7.9]$$

and

$$\sigma_{\bar{x}} = \frac{\sigma}{2} \qquad [7.10]$$

Hence, substituting equations [7.9] and [7.10] into equation [7.8] gives

$$\bar{x}_{min} - \mu_{\bar{x}} = 2(0.82 - |z|)\sigma_{\bar{x}} \qquad [7.11]$$

Now since $\bar{x}_{min}$ is the minimum permissible mean compressive strength of four consecutive test cubes, the probability that a mean-of-four, $\bar{x}$, is no less than $\bar{x}_{min}$ (so that the associated concrete is accepted) is given by

$$P(\bar{x} \geqslant \bar{x}_{min}) = A + 0.5 \qquad [7.12]$$

where area A in Fig. 7.10 can be determined using equation [7.11].

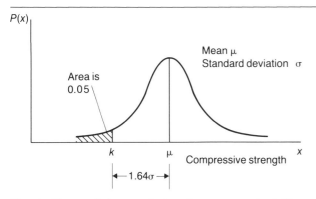

Fig 7.8   Characteristic strength, k, and current margin, 1.64σ

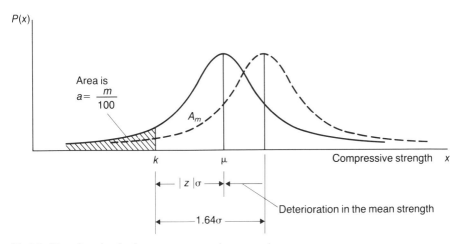

Fig 7.9   Deterioration in the mean compressive strength

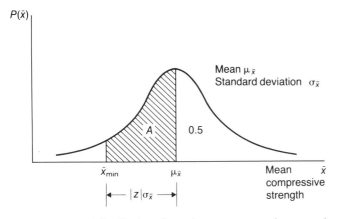

Fig 7.10   Normal distribution of sample mean compressive strength

For example, if the mean strength μ deteriorates so that the defective level is 10%, then the shaded area in Fig. 7.9 is $a = 0.1$. Therefore area $A_m = 0.4$ and hence $z = -1.28$. Equation [7.11] then becomes

$$\bar{x}_{min} - \mu_{\bar{x}} = -0.92\,\sigma_{\bar{x}}$$

so that with $|z| = 0.92$ in Fig. 7.10 area $A = 0.3212$. Thus, from equation [7.12], the probability of accepting concrete with a 10% defective level is

$$P(\bar{x} \geqslant \bar{x}_{min}) = 0.3212 + 0.5$$
$$= 0.8212$$

that is, a 82.12% acceptance level.

Equation [7.11] can be used to determine acceptance levels for various defective levels. The results, when displayed graphically, yield the OC curve for concrete (based on the CP 110 compliance criterion) as shown in Fig. 7.11.

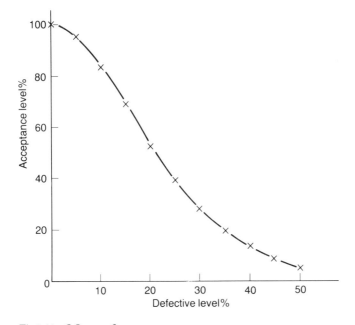

Fig 7.11   OC curve for concrete

7.5   Repeatability and reproducibility

In order to verify that it is satisfactory for a piece of equipment to measure a particular mechanical or physical property of an aggregate, BS 812 (1975) recommends that the results obtained from test samples in different laboratories (i.e. with different measuring equipment) should be checked for consistency, that is, the **reproducibility** should be investigated. Furthermore, consistency of results obtained from test samples in the same laboratory (i.e. with the same measuring equipment) should also be checked. In other words, the **repeatability** should be investigated.

Based on two test results only, BS 812 gives mathematical expressions for measures of repeatability and reproducibility as, respectively,

$$r = 1.96\,\sigma\sqrt{2} \tag{7.13}$$

and

$$R = 1.96\,\sqrt{2}\,\sqrt{(\sigma^2 + \sigma_L^2)} \tag{7.14}$$

where σ denotes the standard deviation of all measurements of a particular aggregate property obtained within a laboratory, and σ_L that of all other variation when measurements between laboratories are compared.

If, when a particular aggregate property is measured, the value of r and R exceeds those given in Table 7.1, then the measuring equipment and procedure should be checked for faults.

Repeatability and reproducibility are now investigated in terms of hypothesis tests.

Consider two infinite populations, A and B, comprising normally distributed measurements of a particular aggregate property obtained in two different laboratories. The respective population means and standard deviations are μ_A and μ_B, and σ_A and σ_B. Samples of sizes n_A and n_B are taken from populations A and B, respectively, and have respective sample means $\bar{x}_A$ and $\bar{x}_B$.

Table 7.1 Repeatability and reproducibility values of various tests for aggregates; after BS 812

Test	Repeatability r	Reproducibility R
Relative density of most aggregates	0.02	0.04
Water absorption	5% of value recorded	10% of value recorded
Bulk density	10 kg/m^3	20 kg/m^3
Aggregate impact value	1.0	2.0
Aggregate crushing value	0.8	1.5
Ten per cent fines value	7 kN	14 kN
Aggregate abrasion value	1.5	3.0
Polished-stone value	4.9	6.0

To investigate the consistency of results obtained in the two laboratories the two populations need to be compared. To achieve this the following question is asked: assuming constant standard deviation, is there any difference between the mean aggregate property of the two populations? Now if a significance level of 5% is considered, then the resulting hypothesis test is

$H_0 : \mu_A = \mu_B$
$H_1 : \mu_A \neq \mu_B$ (two-tailed test)

Test statistic: since both populations are normally distributed the distribution of sample mean differences is normal for both large and small sample sizes, so

$$z = \frac{(\bar{x}_A - \bar{x}_B) - (\mu_A - \mu_B)}{\sqrt{\left(\dfrac{\sigma_A^2}{n_A} + \dfrac{\sigma_B^2}{n_B}\right)}}$$

which, under H_0, becomes

$$z = \frac{\bar{x}_A - \bar{x}_B}{\sqrt{\left(\dfrac{\sigma_A^2}{n_A} + \dfrac{\sigma_B^2}{n_B}\right)}} \qquad [7.15]$$

Rejection region: $\alpha = 0.05$ and two-tailed test. Hence in Fig. 7.12 area $a = \alpha/2 = 0.025$, so that area $A = 0.475$ and hence $z = \pm 1.96$.

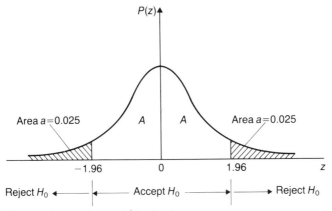

Fig 7.12   Standard normal distribution

Therefore H_0 is accepted at the 5% significance level provided $|z| \leqslant 1.96$, that is, using equation [7.15], $\mu_A = \mu_B$ provided

$$\left| \frac{\bar{x}_A - \bar{x}_B}{\sqrt{\left(\dfrac{\sigma_A^2}{n_A} + \dfrac{\sigma_B^2}{n_B}\right)}} \right| \leqslant 1.96$$

Since the denominator in the above inequality is positive, the results are consistent at the 5% significance level, provided

$$\frac{|\bar{x}_A - \bar{x}_B|}{\sqrt{\left(\dfrac{\sigma_A^2}{n_A} + \dfrac{\sigma_B^2}{n_B}\right)}} \leqslant 1.96$$

that is

$$| \bar{x}_A - \bar{x}_B | \leqslant 1.96 \sqrt{\left(\frac{\sigma_A^2}{n_A} + \frac{\sigma_B^2}{n_B} \right)} \qquad [7.16]$$

(a) Repeatability

Repeatability applies to results obtained from a *single* laboratory (i.e. with the same measuring equipment) and so a single population is involved. Thus if populations A and B are considered to be the same population with standard deviation σ, then $\sigma_A^2 = \sigma_B^2 = \sigma^2$ and equation [7.16] becomes

$$| \bar{x}_A - \bar{x}_B | \leqslant 1.96 \, \sigma \sqrt{\left(\frac{1}{n_A} + \frac{1}{n_B} \right)} \qquad [7.17]$$

Furthermore, with reference to Table 7.1, the values of r are based on a single result from 'each population' (i.e. merely two results, x_A and x_B, from the single population), so that $n_A = n_B = 1$, and $\bar{x}_A = x_A$ and $\bar{x}_B = x_B$. Thus equation [7.17] becomes

$$| x_A - x_B | \leqslant 1.96 \, \sigma \sqrt{2} \qquad [7.18]$$

Hence, using equation [7.13], the results from a single piece of measuring equipment are consistent, at the 5% significance level, provided,

$$| x_A - x_B | \leqslant r$$

where x_A and x_B are results obtained from two test samples and the appropriate value of r is obtained from Table 7.1.

(b) Reproducibility

Reproducibility applies to results obtained from *different* laboratories (i.e. with different measuring equipment) and so two populations, A and B, are involved. Considering the same number of results, n, from each population gives $n_A = n_B = n$. Hence, from equation [7.16], the results obtained from different measuring equipment are consistent, at the 5% significance level, provided,

$$| \bar{x}_A - \bar{x}_B | \leqslant 1.96 \frac{\sqrt{(\sigma_A^2 + \sigma_B^2)}}{\sqrt{n}}$$

that is, with $\sigma_A^2 = \sigma_B^2 = \sigma^2 + \sigma_L^2$ and using equation [7.14],

$$| \bar{x}_A - \bar{x}_B | \leqslant \frac{R}{\sqrt{n}} \qquad [7.19]$$

Now if each piece of measuring equipment provides only one result, x_A and x_B, so that $n = 1$ and $\bar{x}_A = x_A$ and $\bar{x}_B = x_B$, then, for consistency of results between different equipment, equation [7.19] gives,

$$| x_A - x_B | \leqslant R$$

where the appropriate value of R is obtained from Table 7.1.

Example 7.5

A laboratory purchases secondhand equipment for the determination of the polished-stone value. A number of samples of an aggregate are prepared and two are tested giving values of 61 and 64, respectively. A further two test samples are sent to another laboratory which, with its well-used equipment, produced values of 59 and 57. Decide whether or not the secondhand equipment is satisfactory.

For a decision concerning the consistency of measurements obtained with the secondhand equipment the repeatability and reproducibility conditions must be investigated.

(a) Repeatability: $| x_A - x_B | \leqslant r$

This condition is satisfied with polished-stone values from the first laboratory of $x_A = 61$ and $x_B = 64$ and, from Table 7.1, $r = 4.9$.

(b) Reproducibility: $| \bar{x}_A - \bar{x}_B | \leqslant \dfrac{R}{\sqrt{n}}$

For the first laboratory $\qquad \bar{x}_A = \dfrac{61 + 64}{2} = 62.5$

for the second laboratory $\qquad \bar{x}_B = \dfrac{59 + 57}{2} = 58.0$

the sample size $n = 2$ and, from Table 7.1, $R = 6.0$.

Hence the reproducibility condition is not satisfied and so an investigation of the secondhand equipment and measuring technique is necessary. Where a check of the apparatus and procedure does not reveal the cause of the discrepancy BS 812 recommends that further co-operative tests be arranged with additional laboratories.

Exercises

1. A supplier maintains that the mean mass of the flagstones in a large consignment delivered to a housing scheme is 70 kg. Given that three dozen had mean mass 70.5 kg and standard deviation 1.5 kg, decide, at the 5% significance level, whether or not the flagstones are heavier than the supplier maintains.
[Heavier]

2. A machine produces lengths of copper pipe for the building industry and was initially set to give a mean pipe length of 5 m. Given that a sample of 40 lengths had mean length 5.01 m and standard deviation 0.03 m, decide whether or not the mean pipe length of pipes produced by the machine has changed at the 0.05 and 0.01 significance levels.
[Changed, unchanged]

3. Large consignments of building components of the same standard type are delivered to a site. Construct an *OC* curve for the acceptability of a consignment if,

when a dozen components are inspected, a consignment is accepted only if no more than one component is substandard. Hence find the producer's risk if the AQL is 6%.
[0.1595]

4. Repeat Exercise 3 given that a consignment is accepted when no more than two components are substandard.
[0.0316]

5. Use the BS 5328 mean-of-four compliance criterion with $\sigma = 5$ N/mm^2 to construct an OC curve for concrete.

6. Concrete cubes from two mixes were tested for compressive strength. Forty cubes from the first mix had mean strength 39 N/mm^2 and standard deviation 6 N/mm^2. Fifty cubes from the second mix had mean strength 40 N/mm^2 and standard deviation 7 N/mm^2. Decide at the 5% level of significance whether or not there is any difference in the mean strength of the two mixes.
[No difference]

7. Use Table 7.1 to investigate the repeatability and reproducibility of aggregate bulk density values if two test samples with new equipment gave values of 1590 kg/m^3 and 1595 kg/m^3, and a further two test samples with well-tried equipment gave values of 1600 kg/m^3 and 1606 kg/m^3.
[Both conditions satisfied]

Chapter 8

The *t*-distribution

8.1   Introduction

In the sampling considered so far, whether to estimate population parameters (Chapter 6) or to make statistical decisions about a population (Chapter 7), the sample size was large, i.e. $n \geqslant 30$. However, in some situations, due to the time, cost or effort involved in the sampling process, it is not always possible to obtain at least 30 sample measurements. In which case the probability distribution of a particular sample statistic (e.g. sample mean, sample mean difference) might not be described by the normal distribution.

Exactly what probability distribution would describe a small sampling distribution, and under what conditions, is now investigated.

8.2   The t-distribution

Consider large samples taken (with or without replacement) from an infinite population of individual measurements with mean μ and standard deviation σ. Furthermore, suppose that the sample mean, $\bar{x}$, of each sample is calculated, then, as shown in section 5.2 of Chapter 5, the distribution of sample means is normally distributed with mean and standard deviation equal to μ and $\sigma/\sqrt{n}$, respectively, where n is the sample size. Hence for the normal distribution of sample means

$$z = \frac{\bar{x} - \mu}{\sigma/\sqrt{n}} \qquad [8.1]$$

where the probability distribution for z is the standard normal distribution as shown in Fig. 8.1.

However, in practice, when estimating or making decisions, σ is usually unknown and so is replaced by its estimator $\hat{\sigma} = s\sqrt{[n/(n-1)]}$, where s is the sample standard deviation. Hence equation [8.1] becomes

$$z = \frac{\bar{x} - \mu}{\hat{\sigma}/\sqrt{n}}$$

with probability distribution adequately described by that shown in Fig. 8.1.

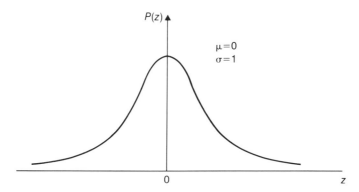

Fig 8.1   Standard normal distribution

Now consider *small* samples ($n < 30$) taken from the original population and, as before, $\bar{x}$ calculated for each sample.

Focusing attention on the quantity $(\bar{x}-\mu)/(\hat{\sigma}/\sqrt{n})$ and in particular $\hat{\sigma} = s\sqrt{[n/(n-1)]}$, it is clear that any individual sample measurement with an unusually large or small value will have a greater effect on the sample standard deviation, s, of a small sample than that of a large sample (similarly for the sample mean $\bar{x}$). Hence, compared to the large sample situation, the value of $\hat{\sigma}$ for small samples will be more variable (because of this the merit of using $\hat{\sigma}$ to estimate σ decreases as n decreases). Furthermore, since $\hat{\sigma}$ is more variable for small samples, then so is $(\bar{x} - \mu)/(\hat{\sigma}/\sqrt{n})$. In other words, for small samples the probability distribution for $(\bar{x} - \mu)/(\hat{\sigma}/\sqrt{n})$ has more variation (i.e. greater standard deviation) than that given in Fig. 8.1 for large samples.

In fact, for *small* samples taken from a population with a *normal* probability distribution and *unknown* standard deviation, it was shown by W.S. Gosset in 1908 that the quantity $(\bar{x} - \mu)/(\hat{\sigma}/\sqrt{n})$ has a probability distribution called a **t-distribution** with standard variable t, where

$$t = \frac{\bar{x} - \mu}{\hat{\sigma}/\sqrt{n}}$$

The probability density function for a *t*-distribution is

$$P(t) = f_1(v)(1 + \frac{t^2}{v})^{-(v+1)/2} \qquad [8.2]$$

where $f_1(v)$ is a complicated function of v with the purpose of making the total area under a *t*-distribution curve unity. The quantity denoted by v, called the **number of degrees of freedom**, is given by $v = n - 1$, where n is the sample size.

Since $P(t)$ depends on v, there is a different *t*-distribution curve for each value of v (and hence n), as shown in Fig. 8.2. Furthermore, as the sample size n increases to 30 and above, the *t*-distribution curves become (effectively) that of the standard normal distribution. Hence the standard normal distribution can be considered as a special *t*-distribution; one in which $n \geqslant 30$.

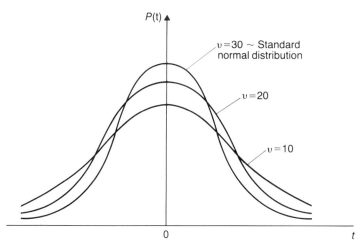

Fig. 8.2 Various *t*-distribution curves, $v = n - 1$

As shown in Fig. 8.2, *t*-distributions have more spread about the mean $\mu = 0$ than the standard normal distribution although other properties remain the same:

(a) they are symmetric about the mean;
(b) the total area under the curve is unity;
(c) the value of *t* gives the number of standard deviations a variable value is away from the mean of its sampling distribution;
(d) the area under a *t*-distribution curve represents probability, e.g. $P(t_1 < t < t_2) = A$, as shown in Fig. 8.3.

Table A.2 in the Appendix gives the values of *t* (i.e. t_a, as shown in Fig. 8.3) for various tail areas a and degrees of freedom *v*.

Note that the conditions for the use of a *t*-distribution are:

(a) the sample size is small ($n < 30$)
(b) the population distribution is normal
(c) σ is unknown (estimated by $\hat{\sigma}$).

However, if σ is known then the normal distribution can be used with small samples provided condition (b) holds (see Examples 5.1 and 5.4).

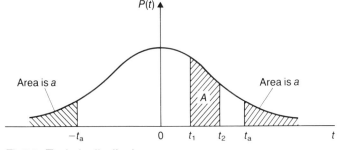

Fig 8.3 Typical *t*-distribution

8.3   *Estimating with small samples*

As shown in the previous section, t is analogous to z for $n < 30$ (for $n \geqslant 30$ t and z are considered to be indistinguishable). Hence, with reference to Section 6.3, the confidence limits for the population mean μ, based on a single small sample, are given by either

$$\mu = \bar{x} \pm t_c \, \frac{\hat{\sigma}}{\sqrt{n}} \qquad \text{with } v = n - 1$$

for an infinite population, or, for a finite population of size n_p

$$\mu = \bar{x} \pm t_c \, \frac{\hat{\sigma}}{\sqrt{n}} \, \sqrt{\left(\frac{n_p - n}{n_p - 1} \right)} \qquad \text{with } v = n - 1$$

where the value of the **confidence coefficient** t_c depends on the specified confidence level.

With reference to Fig. 8.4, if a confidence level of $r\%$ is specified, then area $A = \frac{1}{2}$ $(r/100)$ and so area $a = 0.5 - \frac{1}{2}(r/100)$. Hence with v and a known, Table A.2 in the Appendix gives the associated value of t_c.

The confidence limits for the population mean difference, $\mu_A - \mu_B$, of populations A and B, based on a single sample mean difference is (see Section 6.5),

$$\mu_A - \mu_B = (\bar{x}_A - \bar{x}_B) \pm t_c \sqrt{[(\sigma_{\bar{x}})_A^2 + (\sigma_{\bar{x}})_B^2]}$$

with

$$v = n_A + n_B - 2$$

where, for infinite populations

$$(\sigma_{\bar{x}})_A = \frac{\hat{\sigma}_A}{\sqrt{n_A}}$$

and for finite populations of size $(n_p)_A$

$$(\sigma_{\bar{x}})_A = \frac{\hat{\sigma}_A}{\sqrt{n_A}} \, \sqrt{\left(\frac{(n_p)_A - n_A}{(n_p)_A - 1} \right)}$$

Similarly for $(\sigma_{\bar{x}})_B$.

Example 8.1

For a particular construction project 200 cladding panels were specially made. Given that 25 were measured and found to have mean length 2650 mm and standard deviation 10 mm, determine the 99% confidence limits for the mean length of the 200 panels.

The lengths of the 200 panels (the population) are assumed to be normally distributed with mean μ.

For a confidence level of 99% areas A and a in Fig. 8.4 are 0.495 and 0.005, respec-

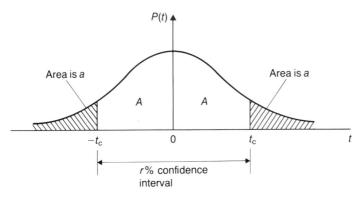

$P(t)$

Area is a

Area is a

A

A

$-t_c$

0

t_c

t

$r\%$ confidence interval

Fig 8.4 Typical *t*-distribution

tively. Thus, with a sample of size $n = 25$, $v = n - 1 = 24$, so the confidence coefficient is $t_c = 2.80$.

Hence with a finite population of size $n_p = 200$ the 99% confidence limits for μ are

$$\bar{x} \pm t_c \frac{\hat{\sigma}}{\sqrt{n}} \sqrt{\left(\frac{n_p - n}{n_p - 1}\right)}$$

which are, since $\hat{\sigma} = s \sqrt{\left(\frac{n}{n - 1}\right)}$

$$\bar{x} \pm t_c \frac{s}{\sqrt{(n - 1)}} \sqrt{\left(\frac{n_p - n}{n_p - 1}\right)}$$

that is,

$$2650 \pm 2.80 \times \frac{10}{\sqrt{24}} \times \sqrt{\left(\frac{175}{199}\right)}$$

that is,

2650 ± 5.36 mm

Example 8.2

A manufacturer produces two types of fast drying paint, X and Y, for interior use only. To compare the paints 8 test samples of plasterboard were sprayed with type X and another 8 were sprayed with type Y. The drying times (in seconds) were recorded and are as follows:

| Paint X | 79.1 | 64.8 | 79.6 | 74.4 | 79.8 | 63.8 | 72.4 | 65.7 |
| Paint Y | 89.3 | 73.6 | 68.0 | 82.5 | 81.6 | 87.0 | 85.4 | 88.2 |

Calculate the 95% confidence interval for the difference in the mean drying times of the two paints.

Using equations [1.3] and [1.6] the mean of the 8 drying times and the estimate of the population standard deviation are, respectively, calculated for each paint,

$$\bar{x}_X = 72.45 \text{ s} \qquad \hat{\sigma}_X = 6.89 \text{ s}$$
$$\bar{x}_Y = 81.95 \text{ s} \qquad \hat{\sigma}_Y = 7.51 \text{ s}$$

With reference to Fig. 8.4, for a confidence level of 95%, area $A = 0.475$ so that area $a = 0.025$. Hence, with $n_X = n_Y = 8$, so that $v = n_X + n_Y - 2 = 14$, the confidence coefficient is $t_c = 2.14$.

The infinite populations of drying times for paints X and Y are assumed to be normal with means μ_X and μ_Y, respectively. Thus the 95% confidence interval for the difference in the mean drying times is given by

$$\mu_Y - \mu_X = (81.95 - 72.45)$$

$$\pm 2.14 \sqrt{\left[\frac{(7.51)^2}{8} + \frac{(6.89)^2}{8}\right]}$$

where, as with large samples (see Example 6.4), the arbitrary subscript labelling is performed in such a way that the difference in the sample means is non-negative. Thus

$$\mu_Y - \mu_X = 9.5 \pm 7.71$$

that is,

$$1.79 < \mu_Y - \mu_X < 17.21 \text{ s}$$

8.4 Test statistics for small samples

The test statistic for a hypothesis test concerning a t-distribution of sample means is

$$t = \frac{\bar{x} - \mu}{\hat{\sigma}/\sqrt{n}} \qquad \text{with } v = n - 1$$

With two normally distributed populations, A and B, the test statistic for a hypothesis test concerning a t-distribution of sample mean differences is

$$t = \frac{(\bar{x}_A - \bar{x}_B) - (\mu_A - \mu_B)}{\hat{\sigma}_{AB} \sqrt{\left(\frac{1}{n_A} + \frac{1}{n_B}\right)}}$$

with

$$v = n_A + n_B - 2$$

where

$$\hat{\sigma}_{AB} = \sqrt{\left[\frac{(n_A - 1)(\hat{\sigma}_A)^2 + (n_B - 1)(\hat{\sigma}_B)^2}{n_A + n_B - 2}\right]}$$

The quantity $\hat{\sigma}_{AB}$ is derived under the assumption that $\sigma_A = \sigma_B = \sigma$ and is called the **pooled estimator** of the population standard deviation σ.

Example 8.3

A building contractor has built a large number of houses of about the same size and value and claims that their average value is £25 000. Six new houses built by the contractor are surveyed and valued at the following prices,

£24 500,   £27 000,   £26 000
£25 000,   £25 000,   £24 800

Decide whether or not the building contractor's claim is conservative at the 5% significance level.

Using equations [1.3] and [1.6], the mean of the six house prices ($n = 6$) and the estimate of the population deviation are respectively

$\bar{x} = £25\ 466.67$ and $\hat{\sigma} = £920.15$

The null and alternative hypotheses are, respectively,

$H_0: \mu = £25\ 000$
$H_1: \mu > £25\ 000$

where μ denotes the mean value of all houses built by the contractor (the population is considered to be 'infinite' and normally distributed). The alternative hypothesis indicates a one-tailed test with rejection region in the positive tail of a t-distribution.

Test statistic

$$t = \frac{\bar{x} - \mu}{\hat{\sigma}/\sqrt{n}}$$

$$= \frac{25\ 466.67 - 25\ 000}{920.15/\sqrt{6}} = 1.24$$

Rejection region: one-tailed test with $\alpha = 0.05$. Hence, with $v = n - 1 = 5$, the critical value of t is $t_a = t_{0.05} = 2.02$ (see Fig. 8.5).

Since $1.24 < t_{0.05}$ the value of the test statistic does not lie the rejection region. Thus H_0 is accepted and H_1 is rejected; that is, the contractor's claim is justified at the 5% significance level.

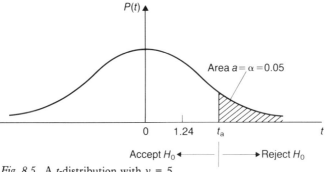

Fig. 8.5 A t-distribution with $v = 5$

Example 8.4

Concrete produced on two adjacent sites, M and N, is designed to have the same target mean strength. Analysis of the compressive strength measurements obtained from 15 test cubes from site M and 10 test cubes from site N yielded the following quantities:

$\bar{x}_M = 38.1$ N/mm², $\quad \hat{\sigma}_M = 6.1$ N/mm²
$\bar{x}_N = 36.4$ N/mm², $\quad \hat{\sigma}_N = 7.3$ N/mm²

Decide whether or not there is any difference in the compressive strength of all the concrete produced on the two sites at the 1% significance level.

In this example

$H_0: \mu_M = \mu_N$
$H_1: \mu_M \neq \mu_N$

where μ_M and μ_N denote the mean compressive strength of all concrete produced on sites M and N, respectively.

The reference to H_1 a two-tailed test is indicated with rejection regions in both tails of a t-distribution.

Test statistic: the compressive strength distributions of the concrete from both sites are considered to be normal with equal standard deviations. Thus,

$$t = \frac{(\bar{x}_M - \bar{x}_N) - (\mu_M - \mu_N)}{\hat{\sigma}_{MN} \sqrt{\left(\dfrac{1}{n_M} + \dfrac{1}{n_N} \right)}}$$

where $n_M = 15$ and $n_N = 10$. Hence, under H_0,

$$t = \frac{38.1 - 36.4}{\hat{\sigma}_{MN} \sqrt{(\frac{1}{15} + \frac{1}{10})}}$$

where

$$\hat{\sigma}_{MN} = \sqrt{\left[\frac{(n_M - 1)(\hat{\sigma}_M)^2 + (n_N - 1)(\hat{\sigma}_N)^2}{n_M + n_N - 2} \right]}$$

that is,

$$\hat{\sigma}_{MN} = \sqrt{\left[\frac{14(6.1)^2 + 9(7.3)^2}{15 + 10 - 2} \right]} = 6.60$$

so $t = 0.63$

Rejection region: two-tailed test with $\alpha = 0.01$. Hence, with $v = n_M + n_N - 2 = 23$, $t_a = t_{0.005} = 2.81$.

As shown in Fig. 8.6, $-t_a < 0.63 < t_a$, so that H_0 is accepted and H_1 is rejected. In other words, at the 1% significance level, there is no difference in the (mean) compressive strength of the concrete produced on the two sites.

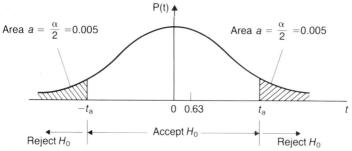

Fig. 8.6 A *t*-distribution with $v = 23$

Exercises

1. A manufacturer of lengths of steel for use in reinforced concrete tests a sample for breaking strength. The results were 2360, 2400, 2380, 2380, 2500, 2450, 2380 and 2400 N. Find the 95% confidence limits for the mean breaking strength of all steel produced.
[2406.25 ± 38.61 N]

2. Four concrete cubes taken from a mix had compressive strengths 35, 32, 33.5 and 29 N/mm². Calculate an interval estimate for the mean strength of the mix at the 90% confidence level.
[$29.37 < \mu < 35.39$ N/mm²]

3. Ten slates were taken from a large consignment and found to have mean thickness 6 mm and standard deviation 0.3 mm. Calculate the 99% confidence interval for the mean thickness of slates in the consignment.
[$5.68 < \mu < 6.33$ mm]

4. The time to complete a new joinery process was measured by two construction firms. The first firm recorded trial times of 37.0, 39.7, 42.6, 40.3 and 37.1 min. The second firm recorded trial times of 43.4, 41.2, 36.9, 39.5, 39.3 and 38.6 min. Find, for the two firms, the 95% confidence limits for the difference in their mean completion times.
[0.48 ± 3.15 min]

5. A machine is set to pack 10 kg of cement powder into bags. A sample of 10 bags is taken and the mean mass is found to be 9.5 kg with standard deviation 0.5 kg. Decide, at the 5% and 1% significance levels, whether or not the machine is in proper working order.
[Not in order, in order]

6. Samples of concrete cubes from two mixes were tested for compressive strength. Cubes from the first mix had strength 34.4, 35.0, 29.2 and 31.9 N/mm², and from the second mix 33.8, 30.5, 34.1 and 27.9 N/mm². Decide whether or not there is any difference in the mean strength of the two mixes at the 0.05 significance level.
[No difference]

The χ^2-distribution

9.1 Introduction

When estimating or performing a hypothesis test the relevant population parameter has been, for both large and small samples, either the mean or mean difference. In this chapter a probability distribution concerning the sample variance, s^2, is considered, together with its use in estimating the population variance, σ^2, and hypothesis testing.

9.2 The χ^2-distribution

Consider an infinite population of measurements which are normally distributed with known variance, σ^2. Now suppose that samples (large or small) of size n are continually drawn (with or without replacement) from the population and the mean of each sample, $\bar{x}$, is calculated. Furthermore, for each sample the quantity χ^2 is calculated, where

$$\chi^2 = \frac{\sum_{i=1}^{n} (x_i - \bar{x})^2}{\sigma^2} \qquad [9.1]$$

and x_i, $i = 1, 2, ..., n$, are the individual measurements comprising the sample. Alternatively, using equation [1.4], the quantity χ^2 can be expressed as

$$\chi^2 = \frac{n s^2}{\sigma^2} \qquad [9.2]$$

where s^2 denotes the sample variance.

Now the distribution of sample χ^2 is a probability distribution called a χ^2-**distribution** with probability density function given by

$$P(\chi^2) = f_2(v) \, \chi^{v-2} \, e^{-\chi^2/2} \qquad [9.3]$$

where $f_2(v)$ is a complicated function of v and $v = n-1$.

As with $P(t)$ in equation [8.2], $P(\chi^2)$ also depends on v, hence there is a different χ^2-distribution curve for each value of v. Various χ^2-distribution curves are shown in Fig. 9.1 where the total area under each curve is unity (this is the role of the function $f_2(v)$ in equation [9.3]).

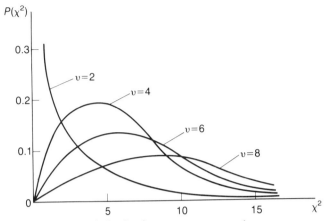

Fig. 9.1 Various χ^2-distribution curves; $v = n - 1$

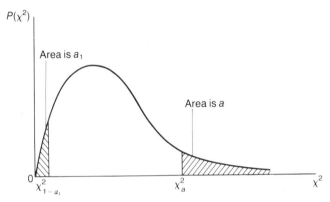

Fig 9.2 Typical χ^2-distribution

A typical χ^2-distribution curve is shown in Fig. 9.2. As with all χ^2-distribution curves it is not symmetric about any vertical axis and, unlike z or t, χ^2 is never negative.

Table A.3 in the Appendix gives values of χ^2 (i.e. χ_a^2, as shown in Fig. 9.2) for various *right-hand side* tail areas a and degrees of freedom v. In other words, since the area under a χ^2-distribution curve represents probability, Table A.3 gives the values of χ_a^2 such that

$$P(\chi^2 > \chi_a^2) = a \qquad\qquad [9.4]$$

If the value of χ_a^2 is required such that $P(\chi^2 < \chi_a^2) = a_1$, where a_1 is a specified left-hand side 'tail' area, then, since $P(\chi^2 > \chi_a^2) = 1 - a_1$, comparison with equation [9.4] gives

$$\chi_a^2 = \chi_{1-a_1}^2$$

that is, the required quantity is $\chi_{1-a_1}^2$ (i.e. $P(\chi^2 < \chi_{1-a_1}^2) = a_1$, as shown in Fig. 9.2).

9.3   Confidence interval for the population variance

As with the population mean and mean difference, a confidence interval for the population variance (and hence the population standard deviation) can be obtained.

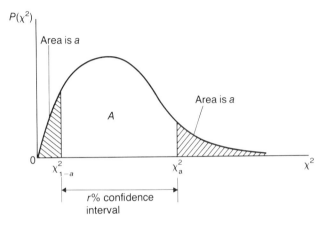

Fig 9.3   Typical χ^2-distribution

With reference to the χ^2-distribution as shown in Fig. 9.3, the $r\%$ confidence interval for a sample value of χ^2 is

$$\chi^2_{1-a} < \chi^2 < \chi^2_a \qquad [9.5]$$

which corresponds to a central area of $A = r/100$ with equal areas either side, i.e. $a = (1 - A)/2$ (since $A + 2a = 1$).

For example, if a sample of size 25 is drawn from a normally distributed population, then the 90% confidence interval for the sample value of χ^2 is obtained as follows.

The areas under a χ^2-distribution curve associated with a 90% confidence interval are $A = 0.9$ and $a = 0.05$. Thus Table A.3 in the Appendix, with $v = 24$, gives

$$\chi^2_a = \chi^2_{0.05} = 36.42$$

and

$$\chi^2_{1-a} = \chi^2_{0.95} = 13.85$$

that is,

$$13.85 < \chi^2 < 36.42$$

at the 90% confidence level.

Using the definition of χ^2 given by equation [9.2], inequality [9.5] becomes

$$\chi^2_{1-a} < \frac{ns^2}{\sigma^2} < \chi^2_a$$

that is,

111

$$\frac{ns^2}{\chi_a^2} < \sigma^2 < \frac{ns^2}{\chi_{1-a}^2} \qquad [9.6]$$

and

$$\sqrt{\left(\frac{ns^2}{\chi_a^2}\right)} < \sigma < \sqrt{\left(\frac{ns^2}{\chi_{1-a}^2}\right)} \qquad [9.7]$$

Inequalities [9.6] and [9.7] are the confidence intervals for the population variance and population standard deviation, respectively, for a specified level of confidence.

Example 9.1

The time to complete a new joinery process was measured in 6 trials with the following results (in minutes):

38.0,   43.1,   39.5,   36.3,   42.7,   39.2

Determine the 95% confidence interval for the standard deviation of the completion time for the process.

If the 6 given trial times (sample size $n = 6$) are denoted by x_i, $i = 1, 2, ..., 6$, respectively, then

sample mean

$$\bar{x} = \frac{\sum_{i=1}^{6} x_i}{6} = 39.8 \text{ min}$$

and sample standard deviation

$$s = \sqrt{\left[\frac{\sum_{i=1}^{6} (x_i - \bar{x})^2}{6}\right]} = 2.42 \text{ min}$$

The infinite population of trial times is considered to be normally distributed so that the sampling distribution of ns^2/σ^2 is a χ^2-distribution. Hence, for a 95% confidence interval, the areas in Fig. 9.3 are $A = 0.95$ and $a = 0.025$. So with $v = n - 1 = 5$,

$$\chi_a^2 = \chi_{0.025}^2 = 12.83$$

and

$$\chi_{1-a}^2 = \chi_{0.975}^2 = 0.83$$

Thus, using inequality [9.7], the 95% confidence interval for the population standard deviation is

$$\sqrt{\left[\frac{6(2.42)^2}{12.83}\right]} < \sigma < \sqrt{\left[\frac{6(2.42)^2}{0.83}\right]}$$

that is, $1.65 < \sigma < 6.51$ min

9.4   Test statistic for the population variance

If, based on the variance of a sample, it is required to decide whether or not the variance of a normally distributed population is as stated (or assumed), then the appropriate test statistic is

$$\chi^2 = \frac{ns^2}{\sigma^2}$$

which has a sampling distribution described by a χ^2-distribution with $v = n - 1$.

Example 9.2

Concrete of grade C35 is used on a construction project for which the designed mean strength is 45 N/mm^2. To investigate the variability of the concrete used on the project 30 cubes were tested and found to have a compressive strength standard deviation of 6.5 N/mm^2.

Decide, at the 5% significance level, whether or not the concrete is more variable than it is designed to be.

In this example the grade C35 concrete has characteristic strength $k = 35$ N/mm^2 and designed mean strength $\mu = 45$ N/mm^2. Hence, since the compressive strength distribution of all concrete used on the project is considered normal with mean $\mu = k + 1.64\sigma$ (see Section 4.4), the variance is, by design,

$$\sigma^2 = \left(\frac{\mu - k}{1.64}\right)^2 = \left(\frac{45 - 35}{1.64}\right)^2$$

$$= 37.18 \text{ N/mm}^2$$

The null and alternative hypotheses are, respectively,

$H_0: \sigma^2 = 37.18$
$H_1: \sigma^2 > 37.18$

where, in the hypotheses, σ^2 denotes the actual compressive strength variance of the concrete used on the project. The alternative hypothesis indicates a one-tailed test with rejection region in the right-hand side tail of a χ^2-distribution.

Test statistic

$$\chi^2 = \frac{ns^2}{\sigma^2}$$

where sample size $n = 30$ and sample variance $s^2 = (6.5)^2 = 42.25$ N/mm^2. Thus, under H_0,

$$\chi^2 = \frac{6 \times 42.25}{37.18} = 6.82$$

Rejection region: one-tailed test with $\alpha = 0.05$. Here $v = n - 1 = 29$ so that, with reference to Fig. 9.4, the critical value of χ^2 is $\chi_a^2 = \chi_{0.05}^2 = 42.56$.

113

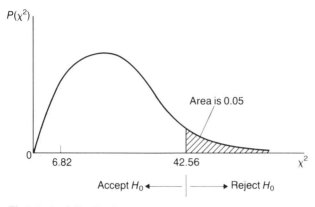

Fig 9.4 A χ^2-distribution with $\nu = 29$

Since $6.82 < \chi^2_{0.05}$ the null hypothesis is accepted and the alternative hypothesis is rejected. That is, at the 5% significance level, the concrete is not more variable than it is designed to be.

9.5 To test goodness of fit

Consider n mutually exclusive events, E_1, E_2, ..., E_n and suppose the number of times event E_1 occurs is counted and recorded as o_1, similarly E_2 occurs o_2 times, etc., then the quantities o_1, o_2, ..., o_n are called the **observed frequencies**. Furthermore, if according to the rules of probability the theoretical number of times E_1 should occur is e_1, similarly E_2 should occur e_2 times, etc., then the quantities e_1, e_2, ..., e_n are called the **expected frequencies** (or **theoretical frequencies**).

The events, observed frequencies and expected frequencies can be conveniently displayed as shown in Table 9.1.

Table 9.1 Observed and expected frequencies

Event	E_1	E_2	....	E_n
Observed frequency	o_1	o_2	....	o_n
Expected frequency	e_1	e_2	....	e_n

From Table 9.1 the quantity

$$\sum_{i=1}^{n} \frac{(o_i - e_i)^2}{e_i}$$

can be calculated. This gives a measure of the discrepancy between the observed and expected frequencies and is zero only when the corresponding observed and expected frequencies agree exactly, i.e. $o_i = e_i$, $i = 1, 2, \ldots, n$. However, in practice

$$\sum_{i=1}^{n} \frac{(o_i - e_i)^2}{e_i}$$

is always greater than zero because some random error between observed and expected frequencies is always present; the greater the discrepancy between observed and expected frequencies the greater is the value of the calculated quantity.

It was shown by K. Pearson in 1900 that for $e_i \geqslant 5$, $i = 1, 2, \ldots, n$, the above quantity has a sampling distribution which can be approximated by a χ^2-distribution. That is, the probability distribution of the statistic

$$\chi^2 = \sum_{i=1}^{n} \frac{(o_i - e_i)^2}{e_i} \qquad [9.8]$$

is a χ^2-distribution with $v = n - 1$ (where n denotes the number of events, i.e. columns in Table 9.1).

To test hypotheses concerning the acceptability of observed data (i.e. its goodness of fit to the expected data) the test statistic given by equation [9.8] can be used to decide whether or not the agreement between the observed and expected frequencies is at an acceptable level. This is achieved by comparing the value of χ^2 given by equation [9.8] with χ_a^2, where χ_a^2 is obtained from Table A.3 in the Appendix and represents the maximum tolerable value of χ^2 associated with data displayed as shown in Table 9.1. In other words, when $\chi^2 > \chi_a^2$, the discrepancy between the observed and expected frequencies is too great (i.e. there is more error than can be accounted for by random error alone). Alternatively, if $\chi^2 < \chi_a^2$, then the discrepancy is at an acceptable level and, at the specified significance level, a null hypothesis of the general type 'the observed data is acceptable' would be accepted.

Hence, as shown in Fig. 9.5, the rejection region for H_0 is $\chi^2 > \chi_a^2$; that is, a one-tailed test. Furthermore, since hypothesis tests concerning the acceptability of observed data always use a one-tailed test, H_0 and H_1 can be stated in words as shown in the following examples.

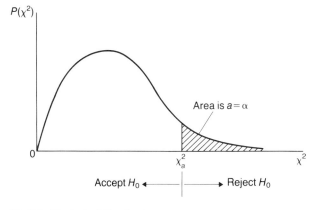

Fig 9.5 Typical χ^2-distribution

115

Example 9.3

The data in Table 9.2 was taken from the records of a certain national construction company and shows the number of employees absent during a particular week (five-day week). Decide, at the 5% significance level, whether or not there is any difference between days of the working week with respect to absenteeism.

Table 9.2 Number absent per day

Day	M	T	W	Th	F
Number absent	34	27	30	29	37

The null and alternative hypotheses are, respectively,

H_0: there is no difference between work days
H_1: there is a difference

The observed frequency o_i, $i = 1, 2, \ldots, 5$, for each day of the working week is the number absent given in Table 9.2. The subscript i denotes the ith day of the working week; hence $i = 3$ means Wednesday and so $o_3 = 30$.

Under H_0 the number absent each day should be in the ratio $1 : 1 : 1 : 1 : 1$. Thus since

$$1 + 1 + 1 + 1 + 1 = 5$$

and the total number absent during the week is

$$34 + 27 + 30 + 29 + 37 = 157$$

the expected frequency for each day is given by

$$e_i = \frac{1}{5}(157) = 31.4, \quad i = 1, 2, \ldots, 5$$

Test statistic

$$\chi^2 = \sum_{i=1}^{5} \frac{(o_i - e_i)^2}{e_i}$$

$$= \frac{(34 - 31.4)^2}{31.4} + \frac{(27 - 31.4)^2}{31.4} + \frac{(30 - 31.4)^2}{31.4}$$

$$+ \frac{(29 - 31.4)^2}{31.4} + \frac{(37 - 31.4)^2}{31.4}$$

$$= 2.08$$

Rejection region: $\alpha = 0.05$ and $v = n-1 = 4$ (since $n = 5$). Hence in Fig. 9.5 the critical value of χ^2 is $\chi_a^2 = \chi_{0.05}^2 = 9.49$.

Since $2.08 < \chi_{0.05}^2$ the value of the test statistic does not lie in the rejection region so that, at the 5% significance level, there is no difference between work days with respect to absenteeism.

Example 9.4

A contractor claims that there is no difference between the daily work rates of a particular gang of bricklayers. The working week for the gang consists of 8 hours per day from Monday to Thursday, 10 hours on Fridays and 4 hours on Saturdays.

The number of bricks laid each day by the gang during a certain week on a large housing scheme are shown in Table 9.3. Decide whether or not the contractor's claim is justified at the 0.01 significance level.

Table 9.3   Observed frequencies

Day	M	T	W	Th	F	S
Number of bricks	4210	4180	4350	4050	5110	1960

The null and alternative hypotheses are, respectively,

H_0: the claim is justified
H_1: the claim is not justified

Table 9.3 gives the observed frequencies, o_i, $i = 1, 2, \ldots, 6$, where, as in Example 9.3, the subscript i denotes the ith day of the working week. For example, o_4 (i.e. Thursday) = 4050 bricks.

Under H_0 the number of bricks laid each day should be in the ratio 4:4:4:4:5:2. Hence since

$$4 + 4 + 4 + 4 + 5 + 2 = 23$$

and the total number of bricks laid during the week is

$$4210 + 4180 + 4350 + 4050 + 5110 + 1960 = 23\,860 \text{ bricks}$$

the expected frequencies are;

Monday to Thursday: $e_i = \frac{4}{23}(23\,860) = 4149.57$

$i = 1, 2, 3, 4.$

Friday: $e_5 = \frac{5}{23}(23\,860) = 5186.96$
Saturday: $e_6 = \frac{2}{23}(23\,860) = 2074.78$

The expected frequencies are presented in Table 9.4.

Table 9.4   Expected frequencies

Day	M	T	W	Th	F	S
Number of bricks	4149.57	4149.57	4149.57	4149.57	5186.96	2074.78

Test statistic

$$\chi^2 = \sum_{i=1}^{6} \frac{(o_i - e_i)^2}{e_i}$$

$$= \frac{(4210 - 4149.57)^2}{4149.57} + \cdots + \frac{(1960 - 2074.78)^2}{2074.78} = 20.67$$

117

Rejection region: $\alpha = 0.01$ and $v = 6 - 1 = 5$. Hence in Fig. 9.5 the critical value of χ^2 is $\chi_a^2 = \chi_{0.01}^2 = 15.09$.

Since $20.67 > \chi_{0.01}^2$ the value of the test statistic lies in the rejection region so that, at the 0.01 significance level, the contractor's claim is not justified.

9.6 Contingency tables

In the goodness of fit test considered in the previous section of this chapter the observed frequencies occupied a single row only. This section considers observed frequencies which occupy r rows and c columns of a table.

For example, if the same type of building component is produced by three machines, A, B and C, and a random sample from each machine is classified into acceptable and substandard components, then the observed frequencies can be displayed as shown in Table 9.5.

Table 9.5 Observed frequencies

| Classification | Machine | | | |
	A	*B*	*C*	*Total*
Acceptable	50	47	56	153
Substandard	5	14	8	27
Total	55	61	64	180

The problem is to investigate a *contingency*, that is, a dependence between the classifications from machine to machine. In other words, does the proportion of substandard components produced by each machine vary from machine to machine. Table 9.5 is called a **contingency table**.

To decide whether or not there is any difference between the machines (with respect to the proportion of substandard components produced) a hypothesis test can be performed with test statistic given by

$$\chi^2 = \sum_{i=1}^{r} \sum_{j=1}^{c} \frac{(o_{ij} - e_{ij})^2}{e_{ij}} \qquad [9.9]$$

with

$$v = (r-1)(c-1)$$

where o_{ij} denotes the observed frequency in the ith row and jth column of Table 9.5 (e.g. $o_{12} = 47$, $o_{23} = 8$), and e_{ij} are the respective expected frequencies which are now calculated.

With reference to Table 9.5,

the total number of components tested $= 180$
the total number of acceptable components $= 153$
the total number of substandard components $= 27$

Therefore

the overall proportion of acceptable components $= \dfrac{153}{180}$

the overall proportion of substandard components $= \dfrac{27}{180}$

Hence for machine A

the total number of components tested $= 55$

thus the expected number of acceptable components is

$$e_{11} = \left(\frac{153}{180}\right) 55 = 46.75$$

and the expected number of substandard components is

$$e_{21} = \left(\frac{27}{180}\right) 55 = 8.25$$

Similarly for machine B,

$$e_{12} = \left(\frac{153}{180}\right) 61 = 51.85$$

$$e_{22} = \left(\frac{27}{180}\right) 61 = 9.15$$

and also for machine C,

$$e_{13} = \left(\frac{153}{180}\right) 64 = 54.40$$

$$e_{23} = \left(\frac{27}{180}\right) 64 = 9.60$$

The expected frequencies are displayed in Table 9.6. The row and column totals are checks since, to within rounding error, they should be the same as those in Table 9.5.

To decide whether or not there is any difference between the machines' output, at the 5% significance level, the following hypothesis test is performed.

H_0: there is no difference between the machines' output
H_1: there is a difference

Test statistic: using the data in Table 9.5 and Table 9.6, equation [9.9] gives

$$\chi^2 = \frac{(50 - 46.75)^2}{46.75} + \frac{(47 - 51.85)^2}{51.85} + \frac{(56 - 54.40)^2}{54.40}$$

$$+ \frac{(5 - 8.25)^2}{8.25} + \frac{(14 - 9.15)^2}{9.15} + \frac{(8 - 9.60)^2}{9.60} = 4.84$$

Table 9.6 Expected frequencies

| | Machine | | | |
Classification	A	B	C	Total
Acceptable	46.75	51.85	54.40	153
Substandard	8.25	9.15	9.60	27
Total	55	61	64	180

Rejection region: with reference to Table 9.5 and Table 9.6, $r = 2$ and $c = 3$, so that

$v = (2 - 1)(3 - 1) = 2$

Hence, since $\alpha = 0.05$, Table A.3 in the Appendix gives $\chi^2_{0.05} = 5.99$. The rejection region is shown in Fig. 9.6.

Since $4.84 < \chi^2_{0.05}$ the null hypothesis is accepted, that is, there is no difference between the machines' output at the 5% significance level.

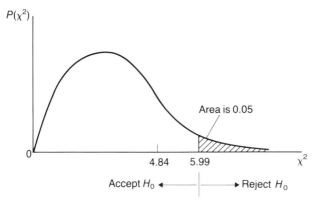

Fig. 9.6 A χ^2-distribution with $v = 2$

Example 9.5

A manufacturer of stoneware pipes (for drainage purposes) has three production processes, W, X and Y, each producing the same type of pipe. Over a period of time samples of pipes from each process were inspected and categorized as shown in Table 9.7.

Decide, at the 0.05 significance level, whether or not the processes differ with respect to the quality of pipes produced.

The relevant hypotheses are

H_0: processes do not differ
H_1: processes differ

With reference to the observed frequencies in Table 9.7,

Table 9.7   Observed frequencies

Category	Process W	X	Y	Total
Acceptable	47	163	38	248
Substandard	14	42	85	141
Scrapped	56	71	12	139
Total	117	276	135	528

the total number of pipes inspected   = 528
the total number of acceptable pipes   = 248
the total number of substandard pipes   = 141
the total number of scrapped pipes   = 139

Therefore

the overall proportion of acceptable pipes $= \dfrac{248}{528}$

the overall proportion of substandard pipes $= \dfrac{141}{528}$

the overall proportion of scrapped pipes $= \dfrac{139}{528}$

Hence for process W the total number of components tested is 117, so that the expected number of acceptable, substandard and scrapped pipes are, respectively,

$$e_{11} = \left(\frac{248}{528}\right) 117 = 54.95$$

$$e_{21} = \left(\frac{141}{528}\right) 117 = 31.24$$

$$e_{31} = \left(\frac{139}{528}\right) 117 = 30.80$$

Similarly for processes X and Y. The expected frequencies are displayed in Table 9.8.

Table 9.8   Expected frequencies (note the effect of rounding error)

Category	Process W	X	Y	Total
Acceptable	54.95	129.64	63.41	248
Substandard	31.24	73.70	36.05	140.99
Scrapped	30.80	72.66	35.54	139
Total	116.99	276	135	527.99

Test statistic

$$\chi^2 = \sum_{i=1}^{3} \sum_{j=1}^{3} \frac{(o_{ij} - e_{ij})^2}{e_{ij}}$$

$$= \frac{(47 - 54.95)^2}{54.95} + \frac{(163 - 129.64)^2}{129.64}$$

$$+ \ldots + \frac{(12 - 35.54)^2}{35.54}$$

$$= 145.78$$

Rejection region: $\alpha = 0.05$ and $v = (r - 1)(c - 1) = 4$ (since $r = 3$ and $c = 3$). Hence the critical value of χ^2 is $\chi_a^2 = \chi_{0.05}^2 = 9.49$.

Since $145.78 > \chi_{0.05}^2$ the processes differ (with respect to quality of output) at the 0.05 significance level.

Exercises

1. During a certain period of time the number of accidents on four similar construction projects were 20, 18, 25 and 17. Decide at the 5% and 1% significance levels whether or not there is any difference between the projects with respect to the occurrence of accidents.
[A difference, a difference]
2. A sales representative for a manufacturer of building components uses the following sample data to convince prospective customers that his products (*A* to *F*) all have the same durability.

Product type	*A*	*B*	*C*	*D*	*E*	*F*
Lifetime (hours)	175	163	168	170	177	173

Decide whether or not his data is convincing at the 0.01 significance level.
[Convincing]
3. Test cubes from a mix with a specified standard deviation of 4 N/mm² had compressive strengths of 33.1, 34.2, 31.7, 36.4 and 39.6 N/mm². Decide, at the 5% significance level, whether or not the compressive strength of the mix is more variable than it is supposed to be.
[Not more variable]
4. The results of the measurement of the degree of conversion of concrete in high alumina cement beams made by two manufacturers, *X* and *Y*, are shown in Table 9.9.

Decide, at the 0.05 significance level, whether or not there is any difference between the manufacturers with respect to the degree of conversion in the beams they produce.
[A difference]

Table 9.9

| | Manufacturer | |
Degree of conversion	X	Y
Slight conversion	41	30
Medium conversion	23	19
High conversion	46	11

5. Three kinds of protection against corrosion were tested by taking samples of a component and applying one of three protection treatments on each sample. The samples were then subjected to corroding agents under identical conditions with the following results.

Table 9.10

| | Treatment | | |
Extent of corrosion	A	B	C
Severe corrosion	9	8	14
Minor corrosion	27	17	30
No corrosion	50	63	47

Decide whether or not there is any difference in the effectiveness of the three treatments at the 5% significance level.
[No difference]

Chapter 10

Quality control

10.1 Introduction

In any production process some variation in the quality of the manufactured product is inevitable. Here 'quality' refers to that of the characteristic property of the product. For example,

(a) variation in the quality of concrete would be with respect to its compressive strength;
(b) with copper piping (for plumbing), variation in quality would be with respect to the diameter.

In this chapter statistical methods are used to monitor the quality of a product in situations where large quantities are produced and 100% inspection is not feasible. An important application in construction is the quality control of concrete.

10.2 Statistical control

Variations in the product of a manufacturing process which are unavoidable and cannot be removed (i.e. random variation) are said to be due to **non-assignable causes**. When subject only to this random variation the process is said to be in a state of **statistical control**.

The quality-control techniques presented in this chapter are used to detect when a process has gone out of statistical control, that is, the product variations are due to **assignable causes** such as,

(a) the machine needs resetting;
(b) a part needs replacing;
(c) the operative needs retraining;
(d) the proportions of constituent materials need redesigning.

In order to detect when an assignable cause of variation is creeping in and causing a process to go out of statistical control, samples of the product are taken at regular intervals and tested. The choice of the sample size will depend on the nature of the production process, the product and the testing technique; the larger the sample size the more reliable the information it gives but the longer it takes to test the items.

A simple, effective and widely used device for analysing and interpreting the data obtained from samples is the **quality-control chart**. Two types of control chart are now presented; those for sample means and sample ranges.

10.3 Quality-control chart for sample means

A control chart for monitoring the average (i.e. mean) quality of a product, that is, a **quality-control chart for sample means**, is shown in Fig. 10.1. On this chart the value of sample means, $\bar{x}$, are plotted against their corresponding sample serial number, i.

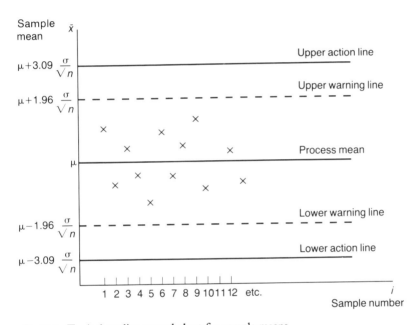

Fig 10.1 Typical quality-control chart for sample means

The use of $\mu \pm 1.96\ \sigma/\sqrt{n}$ and $\mu \pm 3.09\ \sigma/\sqrt{n}$ as **warning and action lines**, respectively, is based on the assumption that the sample means are normally distributed with mean μ (called the **process mean** or **target mean**) and standard deviation $\sigma/\sqrt{n}$, which, for samples of size $n < 30$, assumes that the population distribution is normal with mean μ and standard deviation σ (see Section 5.2).

In Fig. 10.2 a normal distribution of sample means is shown superimposed on a quality-control chart for sample means.

With reference to Fig. 10.2, since $\mu + 1.96\ \sigma/\sqrt{n}$ and $\mu - 1.96\ \sigma/\sqrt{n}$ are both 1.96 standard deviations (i.e. $\sigma/\sqrt{n}$) away from μ, then

125

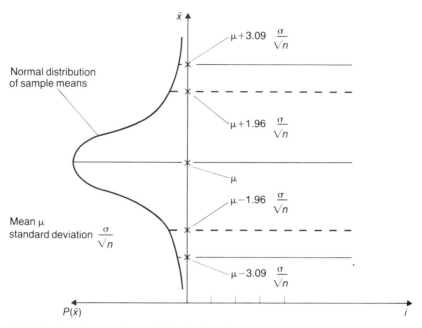

Fig 10.2 Superimposed normal distribution of sample means

$$P\left(\mu < \bar{x} < \mu + 1.96\ \frac{\sigma}{\sqrt{n}}\right)$$

$$= P\left(\mu > \bar{x} > \mu - 1.96\ \frac{\sigma}{\sqrt{n}}\right)$$

$$= 0.4750$$

Hence

$$P\left(\bar{x} > \mu + 1.96\ \frac{\sigma}{\sqrt{n}}\right)$$

$$= P\left(\bar{x} < \mu - 1.96\ \frac{\sigma}{\sqrt{n}}\right)$$

$$= 0.5 - 0.4750$$
$$= 0.0250$$
$$= 1/40$$

In other words, the probability that the value of a sample mean is above the upper warning line (below the lower warning line) is $\frac{1}{40}$. Because of this the warning lines given by $\mu \pm 1.96\ \sigma/\sqrt{n}$ are called the $\frac{1}{40}$ **warning lines.**

Similarly the action lines given by $\mu \pm 3.09\ \sigma/\sqrt{n}$ are called the $\dfrac{1}{1000}$ **action lines**; the probability of the value of a sample mean being above (below) an action line is $\dfrac{1}{1000}$.

When a process is in statistical control the points plotted on a quality-control chart for sample means should, ideally, hover around the process mean between the warning lines. However, when a process is out of statistical control, that is, the actual process mean has changed (the mean quality of the product has changed), the indicators are:

(a) a point above or below an action line;
(b) two consecutive points above or below a warning line;
(c) a run of at least seven points all above, or below, the process mean (this is sometimes called the **rule of seven**).

Hence, based on the quality-control chart for sample means shown in Fig. 10.1, the process appears to be in statistical control (i.e. the mean quality of the product has not changed over the sampling period).

With reference to Fig. 10.1, for samples of specified size n, the location of the process mean, warning lines and action lines requires knowledge of the values of μ and σ. If these population parameters are not specified, then they can be estimated as follows:

$$\hat{\mu} = \frac{\sum_{i=1}^{N} \bar{x}_i}{N}$$

that is, μ is estimated by the mean of the sample means (N is the total number of samples taken), and

$$\hat{\sigma} = \bar{w}A_n$$

where $\bar{w}$ denotes the mean range given by

$$\bar{w} = \frac{\sum_{i=1}^{N} w_i}{N}$$

(w_i are the sample ranges $i = 1, 2, \ldots, N$) and A_n is a constant whose value depends on the sample size n. BS 2846 (1975) gives the values of A_n for various sample sizes; these are shown in Table 10.1.

Hence if μ and σ are unknown the process mean, $\dfrac{1}{40}$ warning lines and $\dfrac{1}{1000}$ action lines are given by $\hat{\mu}$, $\hat{\mu} \pm 1.96\ \bar{w}A_n/\sqrt{n}$ and $\hat{\mu} \pm 3.09\ \bar{w}A_n/\sqrt{n}$, respectively. Furthermore, expressions for the $\dfrac{1}{40}$ warning lines and $\dfrac{1}{1000}$ action lines can be simplified to (using the notation of BS 2846) $\hat{\mu} \pm \bar{w}A'_{0.025}$ and $\hat{\mu} \pm \bar{w}A'_{0.001}$, respectively, where

$$A'_{0.025} = 1.96 \frac{A_n}{\sqrt{n}}$$

and

$$A'_{0.001} = 3.09 \frac{A_n}{\sqrt{n}}$$

Using Table 10.1 the values of $A'_{0.025}$ and $A'_{0.001}$ for various values of n are given in Table 10.2.

Table 10.1 Values of A_n: after BS 2846

n	A_n
2	0.886
3	0.591
4	0.486
5	0.430
6	0.395
7	0.370
8	0.351
9	0.337
10	0.325
11	0.315

Table 10.2 Values of A': after BS 2846

n	$A'_{0.025}$	$A'_{0.001}$
2	1.229	1.937
3	0.668	1.054
4	0.476	0.750
5	0.377	0.594
6	0.316	0.498
7	0.274	0.432
8	0.244	0.384
9	0.220	0.347
10	0.202	0.317
11	0.186	0.294

Example 10.1

Over a period of time concrete cubes from on-site mixes were tested for compressive strength. Table 10.3 gives the sample mean strengths, $\bar{x}$, and the sample ranges, w, for 20 samples of 4 cubes. Construct a quality-control chart for sample means if the target mean strength is 35 N/mm².

From Table 10.3 the mean sample range is

$$\bar{w} = \frac{\sum_{i=1}^{20} w_i}{20} = \frac{126.4}{20}$$

$$= 6.32 \text{ N/mm}^2$$

Since the sample size $n = 4$, Table 10.2 gives

$$A'_{0.025} = 0.476 \text{ and } A'_{0.001} = 0.750$$

Hence with $\mu = 35$ N/mm²,

$\frac{1}{40}$ warning lines: $\mu \pm \bar{w}A'_{0.025}$

$$= 35 \pm (6.32 \times 0.476)$$
$$= 31.99, 38.01 \text{ N/mm}^2$$

Table 10.3 Results from test cubes of concrete

Sample number i	Sample mean $\bar{x}$ (N/mm²)	Sample range w (N/mm²)
1	34.7	7.5
2	37.8	4.8
3	32.1	8.7
4	36.1	6.5
5	34.2	9.2
6	36.4	3.1
7	32.5	10.4
8	35.7	6.0
9	37.2	2.9
10	34.0	5.3
11	34.8	10.2
12	33.3	3.9
13	35.9	6.1
14	34.5	4.5
15	35.7	5.9
16	34.6	11.2
17	32.4	4.6
18	33.8	7.3
19	32.6	5.5
20	33.5	2.8

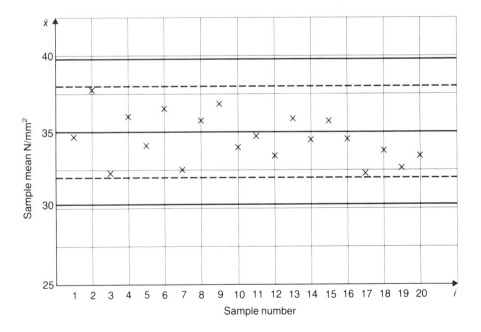

Fig 10.3   Quality-control chart for sample means

129

$\dfrac{1}{1000}$ action lines: $\mu \pm \bar{w}A'_{0.001}$

$$= 35 \pm (6.32 \times 0.750)$$
$$= 30.26, 39.74 \text{ N/mm}^2$$

Using Table 10.3 the quality-control chart for sample means is shown in Fig. 10.3.

Inspection of Fig. 10.3 reveals that all points lie within the $\dfrac{1}{40}$ warning lines and there are no runs of 7 (or more) points all one side of the process mean. Hence the process appears to be in statistical control, that is, the target mean strength is achieved. However, attention is drawn to the last five points; these are all below μ and so, with respect to the 'rule of seven', the results of any subsequent samples could be important.

10.4 Quality-control chart for sample ranges

In the previous section it was explained how a quality-control chart for sample means can be set up and used to detect a change in the average quality of the product. However, it was assumed that the process variance, σ^2, remained constant throughout the production period.

To check that a process variance remains statistically constant a quality-control chart for sample variances can be used. Although a control chart of this type is possible the calculation of the sample variances can be time consuming. An easier and quicker means of monitoring a process variance is to use a **quality-control chart for sample ranges**. That is, the easily obtained sample ranges are used to check the variance of the quality of the product.

A quality control chart for sample ranges is shown in Fig. 10.4, where

mean range: $\bar{w}$

$\dfrac{1}{40}$ warning lines: $\bar{w}D'_{0.975}$ (upper)

$\qquad\qquad\qquad\ \ \bar{w}D'_{0.025}$ (lower)

$\dfrac{1}{1000}$ action lines: $\bar{w}D'_{0.999}$ (upper)

$\qquad\qquad\qquad\ \ \bar{w}D'_{0.001}$ (lower)

Values of the constants D' given by BS 2846 are presented in Table 10.4 for various values of n.

A quality-control chart for sample ranges can be interpreted in the same manner as that for sample means. However, sometimes the lower warning line and lower action line are not used because, in terms of quality control, any decrease in the process variance is for the better.

As seen in Fig. 10.4, unlike a quality-control chart for sample means, that for sample ranges has $\dfrac{1}{40}$ warning lines and $\dfrac{1}{1000}$ action lines that are asymmetric about the

Table 10.4 Values of D'; after BS 2846

n	$D'_{0.001}$	$D'_{0.025}$	$D'_{0.975}$	$D'_{0.999}$
2	0.00	0.04	2.81	4.12
3	0.04	0.18	2.17	2.99
4	0.10	0.29	1.93	2.58
5	0.16	0.37	1.81	2.36
6	0.21	0.42	1.72	2.22
7	0.26	0.46	1.66	2.12
8	0.29	0.50	1.62	2.04
9	0.32	0.52	1.58	1.99
10	0.35	0.54	1.56	1.94
11	0.38	0.56	1.53	1.90

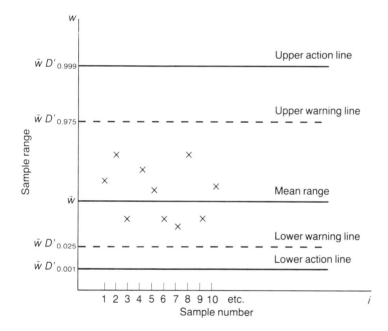

Fig 10.4 Typical quality-control chart for sample ranges

mean. This is because the sample range is used as a measure of the sample variance which, as shown in Fig. 9.2, has a χ^2 sampling distribution whose curve has no axis of symmetry (unlike the normal distribution of sample means; see Fig. 10.2).

It should be noted that, besides the quality-control charts for sample means and sample ranges, others are possible, which, depending on the nature of the manufactured product, may be more appropriate. For example, a quality-control chart for defectives uses the number of defective items (e.g. breakages) per sample to monitor the production process.

Example 10.2

Using the concrete cube results given in Table 10.3 construct a quality-control chart for sample ranges to check that the process variance does not change over the testing period.

From Example 10.1 $\bar{w} = 6.32$ N/mm^2 and from Table 10.4 with $n = 4$,

$$D_{0.025}' = 0.29, \quad D_{0.975}' = 1.93$$

and

$$D_{0.001}' = 0.10, \quad D_{0.999}' = 2.58$$

Hence the $\dfrac{1}{40}$ warning lines are

lower: $\bar{w}D_{0.025}' = 6.32 \times 0.29 = 1.83$ N/mm^2
upper: $\bar{w}D_{0.975}' = 6.32 \times 1.93 = 12.20$ N/mm^2

and the $\dfrac{1}{1000}$ action lines are

lower: $\bar{w}D_{0.001}' = 6.32 \times 0.10 = 0.63$ N/mm^2
upper: $\bar{w}D_{0.999}' = 6.32 \times 2.58 = 16.31$ N/mm^2

The quality-control chart for sample ranges is shown in Fig. 10.5; it indicates that the process variance does not change.

10.5   Cusum charts

With a quality-control chart for sample means, if a particular point lies within the warning lines then it does not *necessarily* follow that the process mean has not changed; an assignable cause of variation may take time to build up to a detectable level so that a considerable amount of time can elapse from when the variation started to its showing up on a control chart.

Because a quality-control chart for sample means does not react quickly to small changes in the process mean the more sensitive **cusum chart** (*cu*mulative *sum* chart) can be used to detect when the process mean has changed.

If successive sample means are $\bar{x}_1, \bar{x}_2, \bar{x}_3, \ldots$ then the corresponding cumulative sums are

$$S_1 = \bar{x}_1 - \mu$$
$$S_2 = S_1 + (\bar{x}_2 - \mu)$$
$$S_3 = S_2 + (\bar{x}_3 - \mu)$$

and, in general

$$S_i = S_{i-1} + (\bar{x}_i - \mu), \quad i = 1, 2, \ldots$$

When the cumulative sums $S_1, S_2, S_3, \ldots$ are plotted against their associated sample

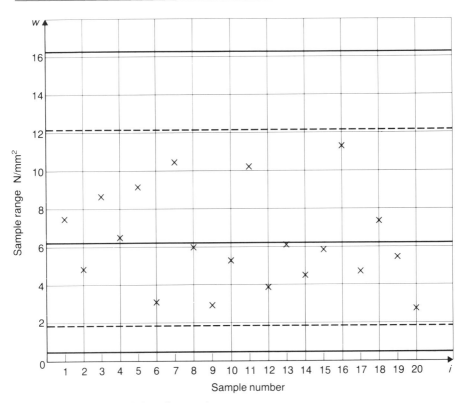

Fig 10.5 Quality-control chart for sample ranges

serial numbers, 1, 2, 3, ..., a cusum chart is obtained. Furthermore, provided the process is in statistical control, the points will hover about a horizontal line through zero.

As shown in Fig. 10.6, if after sample number p the actual process mean increases by a small amount, then subsequent points will have an upward trend. Similarly for a decrease in the process mean subsequent points would have a downward trend. Hence cusum charts are useful for indicating a change in the process mean and when it has occurred.

Furthermore, the slope of the upward trend of cusum values in Fig. 10.6 can be used to estimate the size of the change (i.e. increase) in the process mean, $\Delta\mu$. With reference to Fig. 10.6,

$$\Delta\mu = \frac{S_q - S_p}{q - p}$$

For a downward trend $\Delta\mu$ would be negative.

It should be recognized that the appearance of the slope of the upward trend in Fig. 10.6 is influenced by the scales chosen for the axes. However, BS 5703 (1980) recom-

133

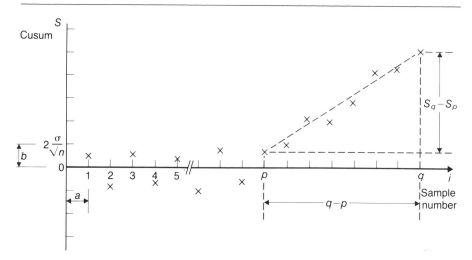

Fig 10.6 Typical cusum chart

mends that the axes are scaled in such a way that if the horizontal distance between consecutive points is 1 unit, then the same distance on the vertical axis represents $2\sigma/\sqrt{n}$ units. That is, in Fig. 10.6, although lengths a and b are equal, in terms of units represented,

$$a : b = 1 : 2 \frac{\sigma}{\sqrt{n}}$$

The cusum chart shown in Fig. 10.6 is idealized; in practice trends may not be so pronounced so that a decision is required as to whether (a) a change of slope can be ascribed to random variation, or (b) it is sufficiently sustained to justify a conclusion that the process mean has changed.

To reach this decision a **V-mask** can be used. This comprises two arms which form a 'V' (drawn on transparent paper or perspex), as shown in Fig. 10.7. A point P is marked at a distance d from the vertex O and the two arms make equal angle θ with the line OP.

Figure 10.8 illustrates the way in which a V-mask is used. As each point is plotted on a cusum chart the V-mask is superimposed with P on the current point and OP parallel to the horizontal axis. If, as in Fig. 10.8, all previous points are within the arms of the 'V' (however far produced) then the process is considered to be in statistical control. However, if a point lies outside the 'V' then this indicates a change in the process mean at around the associated time of sampling.

Obviously the shape of a particular V-mask depends on the values chosen for θ and d. If the axes are scaled as recommended by BS 5703 then it can be shown that with $\theta = 30°$ and $d = 2$ horizontal units the probability of a point being outside the upper arm is $\frac{1}{1000}$; similarly for the lower arm.

134

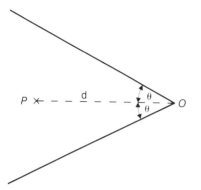

Fig 10.7 Typical V-mask

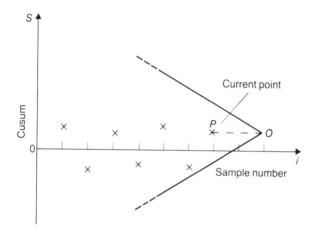

Fig 10.8 Use of a V-mask

Example 10.3

Construct a cusum chart using the concrete cube results in Table 10.3.

For each sample the quantity $\bar{x}_i - \mu$ and hence the cumulative sum $S_i = S_{i-1} + (\bar{x}_i - \mu)$, $i = 1, 2, \ldots, 20$, is calculated. The results are presented in Table 10.5.

Before plotting the cusum values the cusum chart axes are scaled in such a way that the length along the vertical axis equal to 1 (arbitrary) horizontal unit represents $2\sigma/\sqrt{n}$ N/mm², where σ is estimated by $\hat{\sigma} = \bar{w}A_n$. Since the sample size is $n = 4$, Table 10.1 gives $A_n = A_4 = 0.486$. Thus,

$$2\frac{\sigma}{\sqrt{n}} = 2\frac{(6.32 \times 0.486)}{\sqrt{4}}$$
$$= 3.07 \approx 3 \text{ N/mm}^2$$

135

Table 10.5 Cusum chart

Sample number i	$\bar{x}_i - \mu$	Cusum S_i
1	-0.3	-0.3
2	2.8	2.5
3	-2.9	-0.4
4	1.1	0.7
5	-0.8	-0.1
6	1.4	1.3
7	-2.5	-1.2
8	0.7	-0.5
9	2.5	2.0
10	-1.0	1.0
11	-0.2	0.8
12	-1.7	-0.9
13	0.9	0.0
14	-0.5	-0.5
15	0.7	0.2
16	-0.4	-0.2
17	-2.6	-2.8
18	-1.2	-4.0
19	-2.4	-6.4
20	-1.5	-7.9

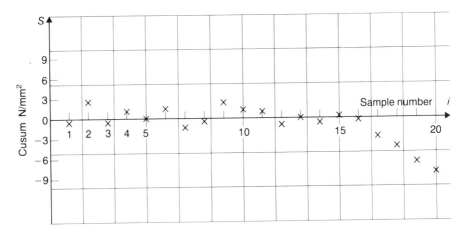

Fig 10.9 Cusum chart

The cusum chart is shown in Fig. 10.9. Notice that the last few points clearly illustrate a downward trend and so draw attention to the possibility that the process may be out of statistical control. Whether or not the trend is sufficiently sustained to indicate that the mean compressive strength of the concrete has decreased can be checked using a V-mask.

Exercises

1. Over a period of time fifteen samples of four concrete cubes from on-site mixes were tested for compressive strength giving the values of the mean strength (28-day) $\bar{x}$ and range w, both in N/mm^2, as shown in Table 10.6. Given that the target mean strength is 33 N/mm^2, use these results to construct a quality-control chart for sample means.

2. Table 10.7 gives the mean diameters and ranges (both in millimetres) of 20 samples of 6 standard lengths of micro-bore copper pipe. Use the first 10 samples to set up quality-control charts for sample means and sample ranges to control future production. Plot the next 10 samples.

3. Concrete is produced on a certain site and over a period of time twenty-two samples of five cubes had mean strengths (in N/mm^2) as shown in Table 10.8. Given that the target mean strength is 30 N/mm^2 and variance is specified to be 5 N/mm^2, construct a cusum chart and use a V-mask to analyse the production process.

Table 10.6

Sample	$\bar{x}$	w
1	34.1	16.0
2	31.4	9.5
3	32.0	14.0
4	35.3	6.0
5	30.1	9.5
6	25.0	15.0
7	24.5	8.0
8	32.5	4.5
9	33.2	2.0
10	35.1	12.5
11	30.1	15.0
12	29.6	3.5
13	34.0	17.0
14	30.3	8.0
15	31.0	6.5

Table 10.7

Sample	Mean	Range
1	4.372	0.10
2	4.324	0.09
3	4.318	0.08
4	4.344	0.04
5	4.346	0.05
6	4.332	0.11
7	4.340	0.09
8	4.344	0.03
9	4.308	0.02
10	4.350	0.06
11	4.370	0.06
12	4.322	0.04
13	4.356	0.10
14	4.322	0.05
15	4.306	0.08
16	4.352	0.11
17	4.332	0.06
18	4.346	0.05
19	4.360	0.04
20	4.374	0.06

Table 10.8

Sample	Mean	Sample	Mean
1	31.23	12	32.31
2	30.10	13	29.40
3	29.23	14	31.30
4	29.97	15	32.83
5	30.51	16	31.68
6	29.08	17	31.63
7	28.36	18	31.44
8	30.77	19	32.48
9	29.42	20	29.95
10	30.95	21	32.10
11	30.66	22	31.45

Chapter 11

Correlation and regression

11.1 Introduction

Statistical methods have, until now, been applied to problems involving one variable only, usually denoted by x, $\bar{x}$ or D (i.e. $\bar{x}_A - \bar{x}_B$). In this chapter problems involving two (or more) variables are considered.

Concentrating mostly on two variables the objectives are,

(a) to determine if they are related in a particular way, that is, is there **correlation** between the variables, and, if this is so,

(b) to express the relationship in **functional form**, that is, as a mathematical equation connecting the variables.

When the values of two variables, x and y, are repeatedly recorded and a functional relationship is known (or assumed) to exist between them then the relationship can be expressed mathematically in general terms as $y = f(x)$, where $f(x)$ represents an expression involving x. The variable x is called the **independent variable** and y is the **dependent variable** (dependent on x, that is).

Different circumstances and physical situations each, in general, yield a different $f(x)$ but in all cases $y = f(x)$ can be used to

(i) predict values of y for values of x outside the data range of x, a process called **extrapolation,**

(ii) determine (approximately) values of y for values of x within the data range of x, a process called **interpolation**.

Some functional relationships are more complicated than others and some have names, for example,

Hooke's law: $y = cx$

where c is a constant and x and y denote strain and stress, respectively. Also

Abrams' law: $y = \dfrac{a}{b^x}$

where a and b are constants and x and y denote water – cement ratio and compressive strength, respectively.

Objective (a) is now investigated.

11.2 Correlation

If x and y denote two variables under consideration, then as a visual aid in the search for a possible relationship between them a scatter diagram can be drawn. As shown in Fig. 11.1, a scatter diagram consists of pairs of sample data values represented as points with co-ordinates (x_1, y_1), (x_2, y_2), ..., (x_n, y_n) with respect to cartesian axes.

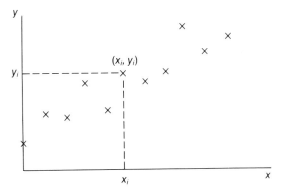

Fig 11.1 Scatter diagram

Inspection of Fig. 11.1 reveals that as the values of x increase so, in general, do the values of y. In other words, the value of one variable is related to some extent to the value of the other variable. Furthermore, the overall pattern of the sample data points (x, y) suggests a possible *linear* relationship, that is, one that can be described by a straight-line graph. The deviation of the data points from a perfect straight line could be due to measurement errors or the influence of other variables not taken into account (or both).

The linear relationship, or **linear correlation**, between two variables can vary from being non-existent to complete, as shown in Fig. 11.2(a) and Fig. 11.2(b), respectively (Fig. 11.1 shows an intermediate case).

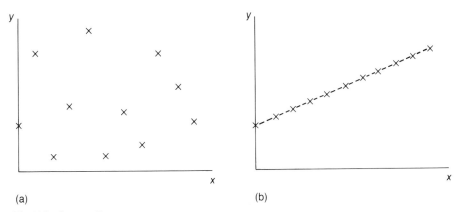

(a)   (b)

Fig 11.2 Scatter diagrams

In order to measure the extent, or strength, of the linear relationship between two variables the **correlation coefficient**, r, can be calculated, where

$$r = \frac{S_{xy}}{\sqrt{(S_{xx} S_{yy})}} \qquad [11.1]$$

with

$$S_{xx} = \sum_{i=1}^{n} x_i^2 - \frac{\left(\sum_{i=1}^{n} x_i\right)^2}{n} \qquad [11.2]$$

$$S_{yy} = \sum_{i=1}^{n} y_i^2 - \frac{\left(\sum_{i=1}^{n} y_i\right)^2}{n} \qquad [11.3]$$

$$S_{xy} = \sum_{i=1}^{n} x_i y_i - \frac{\left(\sum_{i=1}^{n} x_i\right)\left(\sum_{i=1}^{n} y_i\right)}{n} \qquad [11.4]$$

and n is the number of sample data pairs (x, y).

The value of r is such that

$$-1 \leqslant r \leqslant 1$$

If $r = +1 (-1)$ then there is complete positive (negative) linear correlation, that is, in a scatter diagram, all sample data points lie on a straight line with a positive (negative) gradient. If $r = 0$ then there is no *linear* correlation between the two variables. However, it should be noted that $r = 0$ does not necessarily imply that there is no kind of relationship at all; simply that if there is one it is not linear.

For example, with the following sample data pairs,

x	0	1	2	3	4	5	6
y	10	5	2	1	2	5	10

the value of the correlation coefficient is $r = 0$. Hence there is no linear relationship. However, a relationship between the variables does exist but it is nonlinear; $y = x^2 - 6x + 10$, see Fig. 11.3.

In practice the value of r is usually such that either $-1 < r < 0$ or $0 < r < 1$, indicating some negative linear correlation or some positive linear correlation, respectively. In general terms, the nearer the value of r is to ± 1 then the stronger is the linear relationship between the two variables. However it must be realized that the value of r is often calculated from *sample* data pairs only and it could be that the correlation coefficient calculated from *all* possible data pairs (x, y) would be zero.

If ρ denotes the population correlation coefficient, then Fig. 11.4(a) illustrates the case $\rho = 0$. Now if, for example, 6 sample data points are chosen, then Fig. 11.4(b) and Fig. 11.4(c) both show how the value of the (sample) correlation coefficient, r, can be misleading.

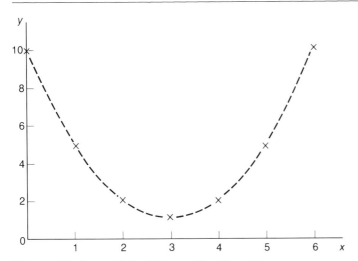

Fig 11.3 Nonlinear relationship: $y = x^2 - 6x + 10$

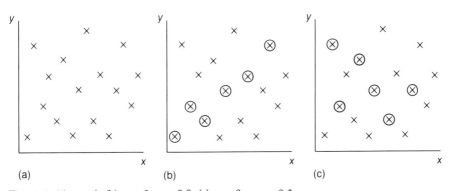

Fig. 11.4 (a) $\rho = 0$; (b) $\rho = 0$, $r = 0.9$; (c) $\rho = 0$, $r = -0.3$

To decide, based on the value of r obtained from n sample data pairs, whether or not two variables are linearly related, the following hypotheses can be used;

$H_0: \rho = 0$
$H_1: \rho \neq 0$

with test statistic

$$t = r \sqrt{\left(\frac{n - 2}{1 - r}\right)} \qquad (v = n - 2)$$

that is, assuming the two variables are both normally distributed, the sampling distribution of $r \sqrt{[(n - 2)/(1 - r)]}$ is a t-distribution with $v = n - 2$.

The alternative hypothesis indicates that a two-tailed test is appropriate and so, at a specified level of significance α, area $a = \alpha/2$ in Fig. 11.5. Hence two variables are linearly related (i.e. H_0 is rejected and H_1 is accepted) provided the value of the test

141

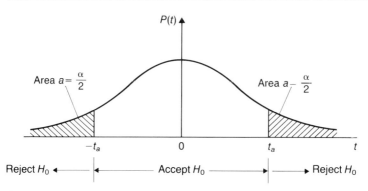

Reject H_0 ← | ← ——— Accept H_0 ——— → | → Reject H_0

Fig 11.5 Typical *t*-distribution

statistic, $r\sqrt{[(n - 2)/(1 - r)]}$, is such that

$$\left| r \sqrt{\left(\frac{n - 2}{1 - r}\right)} \right| > t_a$$

which gives

$$r^2 > \frac{t_a^2}{t_a^2 + n - 2}$$

that is

$$|r| > \frac{t_a}{\sqrt{(t_a^2 + n - 2)}} \qquad [11.5]$$

So, for example, with a sample of 6 data pairs and a significance level of 5%, $v = n - 2 = 4$ and Table A.2 in the Appendix gives $t_a = t_{0.025} = 2.78$. Thus for two variables to be linearly related at the 5% significance level the (sample) correlation coefficient must be such that

$$|r| > \frac{2.78}{\sqrt{[(2.78)^2 + 6 - 2]}}$$

that is,

$$|r| > 0.81$$

that is,

$$- 0.81 > r > 0.81$$

For convenience, **critical values of the correlation coefficient**, r_c where $r_c = t_a/\sqrt{(t_a^2 + n - 2)}$ (see inequality [11.5]), are presented in Table A.4 in the Appendix for various values of v and α.

In the calculation of the correlation coefficient r, given by equation [11.1], precise values of x_i and y_i, $i = 1, 2, ..., n$, are required. However, in some situations the values of the variables x and y cannot be measured with any degree of accuracy. In these situations the x and y data can (separately) be ranked in order of magnitude using the numbers $1, 2, ..., n$ (a tie in data values is overcome by using the mean of the ranks that they would otherwise take). If two variables are ranked in this manner then **Spearman's rank correlation coefficient** is given by

$$r_s = 1 - \frac{6 \sum_{i=1}^{n} d_i^2}{n(n^2 - 1)}$$

where d_i is the difference between the rank values of the data comprising a data pair (x_i, y_i), $i = 1, 2, ..., n$.

Where there are no ties r and r_s are equivalent.

Example 11.1

The rateable values and maintenance costs per month for a random sample of 10 houses are given in Table 11.1.

(a)   Calculate the correlation coefficient r.

(b)   Hence decide, at the 5% significance level, whether or not rateable value and maintenance cost are linearly related for all houses.

Table 11.1   Rateable values and maintenance costs

Rateable value $£10^3$	Maintenance costs per month, $£$
3	23
11	52
7	31
9	41
10	54
15	64
5	24
12	55
10	45
6	23

(a)   With rateable value and maintenance cost denoted by x and y, respectively, the data in Table 11.1 is presented as a scatter diagram in Fig. 11.6.

The scatter diagram indicates that x and y are linearly related to some extent; this extent is now calculated.

Using the data in Table 11.1, Table 11.2 is constructed. Hence equations [11.2] – [11.4] give, respectively,

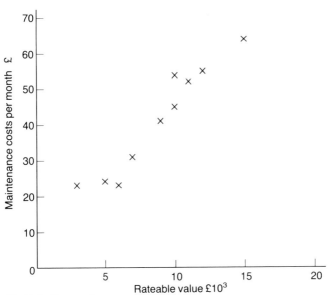

Fig 11.6 Scatter diagram

Table 11.2 Constructed table

x	y	xy	x^2	y^2
3	23	69	9	529
11	52	572	121	2074
7	31	217	49	961
9	41	369	81	1681
10	54	540	100	2916
15	64	960	225	4096
5	24	120	25	576
12	55	660	144	3025
10	45	450	100	2025
6	23	138	36	529
88	412	4095	890	19042

$$S_{xx} = 890 - \frac{(88)^2}{10} = 115.6$$

$$S_{yy} = 19042 - \frac{(412)^2}{10} = 2067.6$$

$$S_{xy} = 4095 - \frac{(88 \times 412)}{10} = 469.4$$

Thus, using equation [11.1], the correlation coefficient is

$$r = \frac{469.4}{\sqrt{(115.6 \times 2067.6)}} = 0.9601$$

which, being close to 1, implies strong positive linear correlation.

(b) If the populations of rateable values and maintenance costs are both considered to be normally distributed then, with hypotheses,

$H_0: \rho = 0$
$H_1: \rho \neq 0$

H_0 is rejected and H_1 is accepted provided

$$|r| > r_c$$

where, with $\alpha = 0.05$ and $v = n - 2 = 8$, $r_c = 0.6319$. Based on a sample of 10 data pairs $r = 0.9601$, so the above inequality is satisfied. Hence, at the 5% significance level, rateable value and maintenance cost are (to some extent) linearly related.

Example 11.2

Given that in Table 11.1 of Example 11.1 the stated rateable values and maintenance costs per month are not exact but are given to the nearest thousand pounds and pound, respectively, calculate the correlation coefficient using Spearman's formula.

As in the previous example, if x and y denote rateable value and maintenance cost, respectively, then, with the x and y values in Table 11.1 ranked in ascending order, the first two columns of Table 11.3 are obtained. The third column is calculated from

$$d_i = \text{rank}(x_i) - \text{rank}(y_i), \quad i = 1, 2, ..., 10$$

Hence with $n = 10$ and, from Table 11.3, $\sum_{i=1}^{10} d_i^2 = 7$, Spearman's rank correlation coeffient is,

$$r_s = 1 - \frac{6 \times 7}{10(100 - 1)}$$

$$= 0.9576$$

Again, strong positive linear correlation is implied.

The difference in the values of r_s and r (in Example 11.1) is due to tied ranks.

Table 11.3 Rank values of x and y

Rank x	Rank y	d	d²
1	1.5	−0.5	0.25
8	7	1	1
4	4	0	0
5	5	0	0
6.5	8	−1.5	2.25
10	10	0	0
2	3	−1	1
9	9	0	0
6.5	6	0.5	0.25
3	1.5	−1.5	2.25
Total			7

11.3 Regression

Once it is established (or assumed) that a relationship exists between two variables, then the next problem is to express the relationship in functional form (i.e. objective (b) in the introduction of this chapter).

(a) Linear regression

Consider two variables x and y, where x is the independent variable and subject to no (or negligible) error of measurement (because of this the variable x is sometimes called the **controlled variable**), and y is the dependent variable which can be subject to measurement error. Now if x and y are linearly related, then the functional form is

$$y = a_0 + a_1 x \qquad [11.6]$$

that is, the equation of a straight line, where a_0 and a_1 are unknown constants (called the **regression coefficients**). For equation [11.6] to be of any use in interpolation and extrapolation the values of a_0 and a_1 are required.

As shown in Fig. 11.7, due to measurement error in the y values the data points do not all (if any) lie on the theoretical straight line given by equation [11.6].

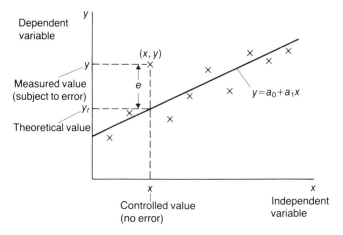

Fig 11.7 Typical deviation, e

Hence the problem is to determine the values of a_0 and a_1 such that with these values $y = a_0 + a_1 x$ is the **line of best fit** to the data points.

In order to determine the line of best fit the **method of least squares** is used. By this method the required line is taken to be the one in which *the sum of the squared deviations, S, is a minimum,* where

$$S = \sum_{i=1}^{n} e_i^2 \qquad [11.7]$$

and n is the number of data pairs.

146

With reference to Fig. 11.7 a typical deviation is given by

$$e = y - y_t \tag{11.8}$$

so that, depending on whether y is greater or less than y_t the value of e is positive or negative, respectively. Because of this the deviations are squared in equation [11.7]; if $S = \sum_{i=1}^{n} e_i$ were considered, then negative deviations could completely cancel positive deviations giving $S = 0$. However, with equation [11.7], $S = 0$ only when each individual deviation is zero, that is, each data point lies on the straight line $y = a_0 + a_1 x$.

In equation [11.8] y denotes a measured value and y_t is the theoretical value given by $a_0 + a_1 x$. Hence

$$e = y - (a_0 + a_1 x)$$
$$= y - a_0 - a_1 x$$

and so equation [11.7] becomes

$$S = \sum_{i=1}^{n} (y_i - a_0 - a_1 x_i)^2 \tag{11.9}$$

The values of a_0 and a_1 are required such that S is a minimum; they are obtained by solving the simultaneous equations

$$\frac{\partial S}{\partial a_0} = 0$$

and

$$\frac{\partial S}{\partial a_1} = 0 \tag{11.10}$$

Using equation [11.9], equations [11.10] eventually yield

$$na_0 + a_1 \sum_{i=1}^{n} x_i = \sum_{i=1}^{n} y_i$$

and

$$a_0 \sum_{i=1}^{n} x_i + a_1 \sum_{i=1}^{n} x_i^2 = \sum_{i=1}^{n} x_i y_i \tag{11.11}$$

that is, two equations for the two unknowns a_0 and a_1. Equations [11.11] are called the **normal equations** for $y = a_0 + a_1 x$ and, with a_0 and a_1 known, $y = a_0 + a_1 x$ is called the **regression line of y on x**.

Using the regression line of y on x the value of y can be obtained for any given value of x (but *not* vice versa).

The **regression line of x on y** can be obtained by interchanging the roles of x and y, that is the functional relationship is

$$x = b_0 + b_1 y \quad (b_0, b_1 \text{ constants})$$

where y is now the independent (controlled) variable and x is the dependent variable (subject to error).

The normal equations for $x = b_0 + b_1 y$ are obtained by minimizing S_H, where

$$S_H = \sum_{i=1}^{n} e_{Hi}^2$$

and e_H denotes a horizontal deviation as shown in Fig. 11.8.

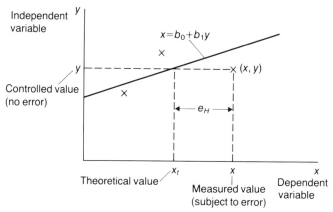

Fig 11.8 Typical horizontal deviation, e_H

With reference to Fig. 11.8, $e_H = x - x_t$ and $S_H = \sum_{i=1}^{n} (x_i - b_0 - b_1 y_i)^2$, so that $\partial S_H/\partial b_0 = 0$ and $\partial S_H/\partial b_1 = 0$ give, respectively,

$$n b_0 + b_1 \sum_{i=1}^{n} y_i = \sum_{i=1}^{n} x_i$$

$$b_0 \sum_{i=1}^{n} y_i + b_1 \sum_{i=1}^{n} y_i^2 = \sum_{i=1}^{n} x_i y_i$$

that is, the normal equations for $x = b_0 + b_1 y$ which yield b_0 and b_1. The regression line of x on y is used to obtain values of x for given values of y (but *not* vice versa).

When it is not obvious which variable is the independent variable then both regression lines should be calculated. For a particular set of n data pairs (x, y) the regression lines of y on x and x on y do not coincide but, as shown in Fig. 11.9, intersect at the point $(\bar{x}, \bar{y})$, where

$$\bar{x} = \frac{\sum_{i=1}^{n} x_i}{n} \quad \text{and} \quad \bar{y} = \frac{\sum_{i=1}^{n} y_i}{n}$$

In general, the greater the linear correlation between the variables x and y the closer the two regression lines become; they coincide for complete linear correlation only (i.e. $r = \pm 1$).

148

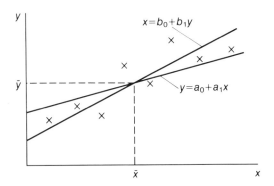

Fig 11.9 Regression lines of y on x and x on y

Example 11.3

Use the data in Table 11.1 of Example 11.1 to determine the regression lines of y on x and x on y (where x and y denote rateable value and maintenance costs per month, respectively).

The normal equations for the regression line of y on x, $y = a_0 + a_1 x$, are given by equations [11.11],

$$n a_0 + a_1 \sum_{i=1}^{n} x_i = \sum_{i=1}^{n} y_i$$

$$a_0 \sum_{i=1}^{n} x_i + a_1 \sum_{i=1}^{n} x_i^2 = \sum_{i=1}^{n} x_i y_i$$

which, using the data in Table 11.2, become

$10a_0 + 88a_1 = 412$
$88a_0 + 890a = 4095$

Solving the normal equations simultaneously gives

$a_0 = 5.47$ and $a_1 = 4.06$

thus the regression line of y on x is

$y = 5.47 + 4.06x$

If a rateable value is specified, then this equation gives the maintenance costs per month. For example, a house with rateable value £8000, i.e. $x = 8$, would have maintenance costs per month given (approximately) by

$y = 5.47 + 4.06 \times 8$
$\quad = £37.95$

For the regression line of x on y, $x = b_0 + b_1 y$, the normal equations are

149

$$nb_0 + b_1 \sum_{i=1}^{n} y_i = \sum_{i=1}^{n} x_i$$

$$b_0 \sum_{i=1}^{n} y_i + b_1 \sum_{i=1}^{n} y_i^2 = \sum_{i=1}^{n} x_i y_i$$

that is, from Table 11.2,

$$10b_0 + 412b_1 \quad = 88$$
$$412b_0 + 19042b_1 \quad = 4095$$

These yield,

$$b_0 = -0.55 \quad \text{and} \quad b_1 = 0.23$$

and so the regression line of x on y is

$$x = -0.55 + 0.23y$$

which gives the rateable value for a specified maintenance cost per month.

For example, if the maintenance costs per month for a house are $y = £35$, then the rateable value is (approximately),

$$x = -0.55 + 0.23 \times 35$$
$$= 7.5$$

that is,

$$x = £7500$$

(b) Polynomial regression

The ideas of the previous subsection can be extended to deal with polynomial functional relationships between two variables. That is, if x and y are the independent and dependent variables, respectively, then the mathematical equation relating them could be,

$$y = a_0 + a_1 x + a_2 x^2$$

a quadratic regression curve, or

$$y = a_0 + a_1 x + a_2 x^2 + a_3 x^3$$

a cubic regression curve, or, in general,

$$y = a_0 + a_1 x + \ldots + a_n x^n$$

which represents a polynomial regression curve of the nth degree, where $a_0, a_1 \ldots, a_n$ are the unknown regression coefficients.

If, for example, a relationship of the form $y = a_0 + a_1 x + a_2 x^2$ exists between variables x and y, and n data pairs are considered, then Fig. 11.10 shows a typical data point on a scatter diagram.

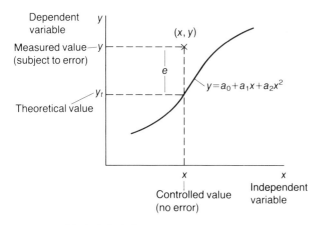

Fig 11.10 Typical deviation, *e*

As before the deviation is $e = y - y_t$, but now y_t is given by $a_0 + a_1 x + a_2 x^2$, so that

$$e = y - a_0 - a_1 x - a_2 x^2$$

and so the sum of the squared deviations, S, is given by

$$S = \sum_{i=1}^{n} (y_i - a_0 - a_1 x_i - a_2 x_i^2)^2 \qquad [11.12]$$

For the method of least squares the quadratic polynomial of best fit is the one whose values of a_0, a_1 and a_2 are such that S is a minimum; these values are obtained by solving simultaneously,

$$\frac{\partial S}{\partial a_0} = 0, \qquad \frac{\partial S}{\partial a_1} = 0, \qquad \frac{\partial S}{\partial a_2} = 0 \qquad [11.13]$$

From equations [11.12] and [11.13] the following normal equations for $y = a_0 + a_1 x + a_2 x^2$ are obtained:

$$n a_0 + a_1 \sum_{i=1}^{n} x_i + a_2 \sum_{i=1}^{n} x_i^2 = \sum_{i=1}^{n} y_i$$

$$a_0 \sum_{i=1}^{n} x_i + a_1 \sum_{i=1}^{n} x_i^2 + a_2 \sum_{i=1}^{n} x_i^3 = \sum_{i=1}^{n} x_i y_i$$

$$a_0 \sum_{i=1}^{n} x_i^2 + a_1 \sum_{i=1}^{n} x_i^3 + a_2 \sum_{i=1}^{n} x_i^4 = \sum_{i=1}^{n} x_i^2 y_i$$

that is, three equations for the three unknowns a_0, a_1 and a_2.

The normal equations for polynomials of higher degree can be obtained in a similar manner with the number of simultaneous equations comprising the normal equations equal to the number of unknown regression coefficients.

151

Example 11.4

The first six weeks cumulative costs for a certain construction project are

Week	1	2	3	4	5	6
Cost £10³	5	10	16	26	34	40

Given that the week number (x) and cumulative costs (y) are related by the equation

$$y = ax^2 + bx$$

determine the cumulative cost in week 9.

The normal equations for $y = ax^2 + bx$ can be obtained in the usual manner by the method of least squares, that is, using

$$S = \sum_{i=1}^{6} (y_i - ax_i^2 - bx_i)^2$$

with

$$\frac{\partial S}{\partial a} = 0 \quad \text{and} \quad \frac{\partial S}{\partial b} = 0$$

These yield, respectively,

$$a \sum_{i=1}^{6} x_i^4 + b \sum_{i=1}^{6} x_i^3 = \sum_{i=1}^{6} x_i^2 y_i$$

$$a \sum_{i=1}^{6} x_i^3 + b \sum_{i=1}^{6} x_i^2 = \sum_{i=1}^{6} x_i y_i$$

Table 11.4 Constructed table

x	y	xy	x^2	$x^2 y$	x^3	x^4
1	5	5	1	5	1	1
2	10	20	4	40	8	16
3	16	48	9	144	27	81
4	26	104	16	416	64	256
5	34	170	25	850	125	625
6	40	240	36	1440	216	1296
Sums		587	91	2895	441	2275

Using the data in Table 11.4 the normal equations become

$$2275a + 441b = 2895$$
$$441a + 91b = 587$$

Solving simultaneously gives

$$a = 0.36 \text{ and } b = 4.68$$

so that

$y = 0.36x^2 + 4.68x$

Thus the cumulative cost in week 9 is

$y = 0.36(9)^2 + 4.68(9)$
   $= 71.28$
   $= £71\ 280$

In the calculation of the cumulative cost in week 9 it is assumed that the given relationship between x and y (i.e. $y = ax^2 + bx$) persists beyond the data range of x, that is, beyond week 6. The validity of this assumption depends on the length of the construction project; in the initial stages $y = ax^2 + bx$ can describe the weekly cumulative costs, but usually an 'S' curve describes the entire project (see Fig. 11.11).

This example emphasizes the dangers inherent in extrapolation.

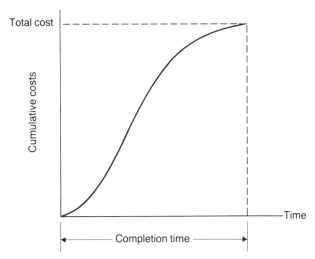

Fig 11.11 Typical cost – time curve

(c) Multiple regression

So far in this study of regression only two variables have been considered. In this subsection a dependent variable y is considered to be a function of *two* independent variables, x_1 and x_2; for example,

$y = a_0 + a_1 x_1 + a_2 x_2$

With m independent variables $x_1, x_2, ..., x_m$ the functional relationship can be generalized to

$y = a_0 + a_1 x_1 + ... \, a_m x_m$

where $a_0, a_1, ..., a_m$ are the unknown regression coefficients.

153

If n data triplets (x_1, x_2, y) are considered, then to determine the normal equations for $y = a_0 + a_1 x_1 + a_2 x_2$ (whereby a_0, a_1 and a_2 are determined) the usual method of least squares procedure is followed;

$$e = y - (a_0 + a_1 x_1 + a_2 x_2)$$

so that,

$$S = \sum_{i=1}^{n} (y_i - a_0 - a_1 (x_1)_i - a_2 (x_2)_i)^2$$

Hence $\partial S / \partial a_0 = 0$, $\partial S / \partial a_1 = 0$ and $\partial S / \partial a_2 = 0$ yield, respectively,

$$n\, a_0 + a_1 \sum_{i=1}^{n} (x_1)_i + a_2 \sum_{i=1}^{n} (x_2)_i = \sum_{i=1}^{n} y_i$$

$$a_0 \sum_{i=1}^{n} (x_1)_i + a_1 \sum_{i=1}^{n} (x_1)_i^2 + a_2 \sum_{i=1}^{n} (x_1)_i (x_2)_i = \sum_{i=1}^{n} (x_1)_i y_i$$

$$a_0 \sum_{i=1}^{n} (x_2)_i + a_1 \sum_{i=1}^{n} (x_1)_i (x_2)_i + a_2 \sum_{i=1}^{n} (x_2)_i^2 = \sum_{i=1}^{n} (x_2)_i y_i$$

The normal equations for functional relationships of the form

$$y = a_0 + a_1 x_1 + a_2 x_2 + a_3 x_1 x_2$$

can be obtained in a similar manner; the interaction expression $x_1 x_2$ is treated as though it were a new independent variable, x_3, i.e. let $x_3 = x_1 x_2$.

11.4 Abrams' law for concrete strength

For fully compacted concrete D. Abrams established (in 1919) that the compressive strength, y, can be expressed in terms of the water – cement ratio of the mix, x, by the equation

$$y = \frac{a}{b^x} \qquad\qquad [11.14]$$

where a and b are empirical constants.

Equation [11.14] is an example of a nonlinear relationship between two variables and, in terms of regression, is of a form not previously considered.

If, as it stands, equation [11.14] is used to determine its associated normal equations then, although this is possible (in principle, at least), unfortunately, they are too complicated to solve for a and b.

However, if the logarithm (any base) of both sides of equation [11.14] is taken, then

$$\log y = \log \left(\frac{a}{b^x} \right)$$

$$= \log a - \log (b^x)$$
$$= \log a - (\log b)x$$

Hence, under the transformation,

$$\log y \leftrightarrow y$$
$$\log a \leftrightarrow a_0 \qquad\qquad\qquad\qquad [11.15]$$
$$- \log b \leftrightarrow a_1$$
$$x \leftrightarrow x$$

the original nonlinear relationship is reduced to a linear one; $y = a_0 + a_1 x$. The normal equations for the regression line of y on x are given by equations [11.11]. Thus, applying transformation [11.15], the normal equations for $y = a/b^x$ are

$$n \log a - \log b \sum_{i=1}^{n} x_i = \sum_{i=1}^{n} \log y_i$$

$$\log a \sum_{i=1}^{n} x_i - \log b \sum_{i=1}^{n} x_i^2 = \sum_{i=1}^{n} x_i \log y_i$$

The above equations can be solved for $\log a$ and $\log b$ and so, in turn, a and b are determined.

A similar procedure whereby a nonlinear relationship is reduced to a linear one can be applied to equations of the form

$$y = a\, e^{bx}$$
$$y = a\, x^b$$

and

$$y = a\, b^x$$

Example 11.5

Determine Abrams' law for the following water – cement ratios (x) and compressive strengths (y N/mm²).

x	0.4	0.5	0.6	0.7	0.8	0.9
y	48.2	36.9	29.4	22.0	15.7	11.6

Hence determine the compressive strength of concrete with a water – cement ratio of 0.55.

Using the given values of x and y Table 11.5 is constructed.

Table 11.5 Constructed table

x	y	$\ln y$	$x \ln y$	x^2
0.4	48.2	3.8754	1.5502	0.16
0.5	36.9	3.6082	1.8041	0.25
0.6	29.4	3.3810	2.0286	0.36
0.7	22.0	3.0910	2.1637	0.49
0.8	15.7	2.7537	2.2030	0.64
0.9	11.6	2.4510	2.2059	0.81
3.9	−	19.1603	11.9555	2.71

Hence the normal equations for $y = a/b^x$ are

$6 \ln a - 3.9 \ln b = 19.1603$
$3.9 \ln a - 2.71 \ln b = 11.9555$

which yield

$\ln a = 5.0457$ and $\ln b = 2.8497$

that is

$a = e^{5.0457} = 155.35$

and

$b = e^{2.8497} = 17.28$

Hence for the given data Abrams' law is

$$y = \frac{155.35}{(17.28)^x}$$

and, for $x = 0.55$,

$$y = \frac{155.35}{(17.28)^{0.55}} = 32.41 \text{ N/mm}^2$$

11.5 Confidence intervals

Consider two variables, x and y, in which y, unlike x, is subject to measurement error. Furthermore, if sample data points are considered then, as shown in Fig. 11.12, for a particular value of x there are an infinite number of possible y-observations. The mean of the population of y-observations is the true value of y at x. The graph of such y-means for all values of x represents the functional relationship between variables x and y (the true regression line of y on x, see Fig. 11.12).

When a functional relationship exists between x and y the variation in the y-observations about the mean (at particular values of x) would be caused solely by measurement errors. When no such relationship exists the presence of other effects would also contribute to the variation in y.

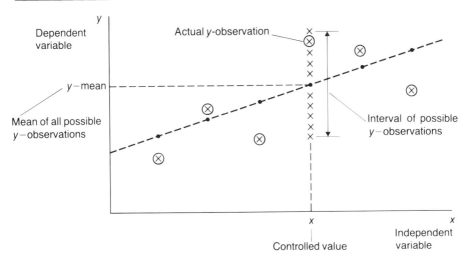

Fig 11.12   Possible *y*-observations at a particular value of *x*

The regression line of y on x is represented by the straight-line graph of y-means against *all* x-values. However, this line exists in theory only because in practice only a finite number of data pairs (x, y) are available (as opposed to the infinite number required to give the true regression line of y on x). In other words, the (population) regression line of y on x shown in Fig. 11.12 can be expressed as

$$y = \alpha_0 + \alpha_1 x$$

where α_0 and α_1 are the population (i.e. true) regression coefficients, but with only a finite number of data pairs the (sample) regression line of y on x is

$$y = a_0 + a_1 x$$

where the values of a_0 and a_1 are determined by the method of least squares (as shown in the previous section of this chapter) and are used as point estimates of α_0 and α_1 (which are impossible to determine), respectively, that is,

$$\hat{\alpha}_0 = a_0, \qquad \hat{\alpha}_1 = a_1$$

Note that for a given value of x the (sample) regression line of y on x, $y = a_0 + a_1 x$, gives the (estimated) mean value of the population of y-observations. Furthermore, the underlying assumption of the (population) regression line of y on x is that for each value of x the distribution of y-observations is normal with the same standard deviation, as shown in Fig. 11.13.

The most common purpose of calculating the regression line of y on x is to use it to make predictions about the value of y at any given value of x. That is, the value of $\alpha_0 + \alpha_1 x$ is required (where, at a particular value of x, $\alpha_0 + \alpha_1 x$ is the mean of the normal distribution of y-observations). However, since α_0 and α_1 are unknown they are estimated by a_0 and a_1, respectively, so that $a_0 + a_1 x$ is a point estimate of $\alpha_0 + \alpha_1 x$.

Now if the sampling distributions of a_0, a_1 and hence, at particular values of x, $a_0 +$

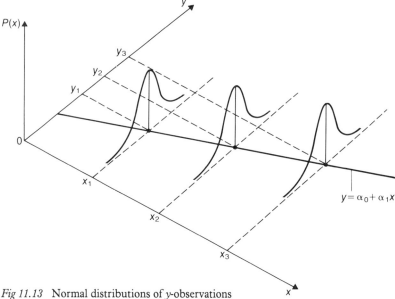

Fig 11.13 Normal distributions of *y*-observations

$a_1 x$, are considered to be normal, then, with n data pairs, the confidence limits for the mean of the normal distribution of *y*-observations are given by

$$(a_0 + a_1 x) \pm t_c \hat{\sigma} \sqrt{\left[\frac{1}{n} + \frac{(x - \bar{x})^2}{S_{xx}} \right]}$$ [11.16]

where, at a specified confidence level, t_c is the confidence coefficient ($v = n - 2$),

$$\hat{\sigma} = \sqrt{\left[\frac{\sum_{i=1}^{n} (y_i - a_0 - a_1 x_i)^2}{n - 2} \right]}$$ [11.17]

and

$$S_{xx} = \sum_{i=1}^{n} (x_i - \bar{x})^2$$ [11.18]

It should be stressed that the above confidence limits apply, at a particular value of x, to the *y*-mean only. The confidence limits for an individual *y*-observation at a particular value of x, called the **prediction limits**, are given by

$$(a_0 + a_1 x) \pm t_c \hat{\sigma} \sqrt{\left[1 + \frac{1}{n} + \frac{(x - \bar{x})^2}{S_{xx}} \right]}$$ [11.19]

Typical loci of the confidence limits given by expressions [11.16] and [11.19] are shown as curves in Fig. 11.14. Notice that the confidence intervals for the mean of the distribution of *y*-observations and for an individual *y*-observation are both minimum when $x = \bar{x}$ (i.e. when the $(x - \bar{x})^2$ term in expressions [11.16] and [11.19] is zero).

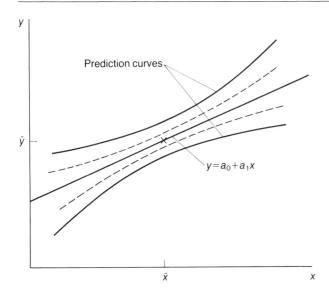

Fig 11.14 Calculated regression line of y on x and confidence curves

Example 11.6

The extensions (y mm) of a specimen of steel rod under various loads (x kN) are found to be

x	1	2	3	4	5
y	15	32	45	63	77

Determine, for a load of 4.5 kN, the 90% prediction interval for the extension.

Using the given data with x as the independent variable and y as the dependent variable the regression line of y on x can be shown to be

$$y = -0.1 + 15.5x$$

Hence equation [11.17] with $n = 5$ gives

$$\hat{\sigma} = \sqrt{\left[\frac{\sum_{i=1}^{5} (y_i + 0.1 - 15.5x_i)^2}{3} \right]}$$

$$= 1.25 \text{ mm}$$

The mean of the x values is

$$\bar{x} = \frac{\sum_{i=1}^{5} x_i}{5} = \frac{15}{5} = 3 \text{ kN}$$

159

and so, from equation [11.18],

$$S_{xx} = \sum_{i=1}^{5} (x_i - 3)^2 = 10 \text{ kN}$$

Thus, using expression [11.19], for a particular load x the prediction interval for the extension is

$$y = (-0.1 + 15.5x) \pm t_c \, 1.25 \sqrt{\left[1 + \frac{1}{5} + \frac{(x - 3)^2}{10}\right]}$$

where, for a 90% confidence level and $v = n - 2 = 3$, $t_c = 2.35$. So for $x = 4.5$ kN,

$y = 69.65 \pm 3.51$ mm

that is,

$66.14 < y < 73.16$ mm.

Exercises

1. A random sample of 8 carpenters had the following heights (H cm) and masses (M kg),

H	160.0	180.3	182.7	172.9	190.5	167.6	172.7	193.8
M	65.8	71.7	70.8	67.2	74.0	70.4	69.5	71.7

(a) Calculate the correlation coefficient.
(b) Based on the above sample decide, at the 5% significance level, whether or not the relationship between the height and weight of carpenters is linear.
[(a) 0.7912, (b) linear relationship]

2. For a sample of consignments of bricks delivered to various building sites the delivery time (T-hours) and distance travelled (D km) were as shown:

D	64	82	145	102	96	48	120	87	153	99
T	1.1	1.8	2.2	2.1	1.4	0.6	2.2	1.6	3.0	1.6

(a) Calculate the regression lines of T on D and D on T.
(b) Calculate the correlation coefficient.
(c) Decide whether or not the variables D and T are linearly related at the 5% significance level.
[(a) $T = -0.100 + 0.019D$, $D = 19.58 + 45.46T$, (b) 0.9215, (c) linear relationship]

3. A manufacturer produces a certain building component of standard length L (m) and cost C (£) as shown:

L	1	2	3	4	5
C	5	10	20	35	50

Given that the manufacturer proposes to produce a component of length 7.5 m find its approximate cost if the variables are related by $C = a + bL^2$ (a and b are constants). [£110.4]

4. Determine Abrams' law for the following water–cement ratios (R) and compressive strengths $(S\ \text{N/mm}^2)$:

R	0.4	0.5	0.6	0.7	0.8	0.9
S	50.3	37.2	29.9	25.1	16.8	12.3

$[S = 153.11\,(15.55)^{-R}]$

5. The maximum deflections $(D\ \text{mm})$ of a beam under increasing loads $(W\ \text{kN})$ are

W	1.0	1.25	1.5	1.75	2.0
D	9.1	10.2	10.9	11.8	13.1

(a) Find the regression line of D on W.
(b) For a load of 1.8 kN calculate the prediction limits for the maximum deflection at the 90% confidence level.
   [(a) $D = 5.26 + 3.84\ W$, (b) 12.17 ± 0.48 mm]

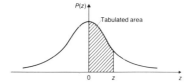

P(z)

Tabulated area

0   z   z

Appendix

Table A.1 Areas under the standard normal distribution curve from 0 to z. (Reproduced from Appendix II of M.R. Spiegel, *Theory and Problems of Statistics*, McGraw-Hill, 1972)

z	0	1	2	3	4	5	6	7	8	9
0.0	0.0000	0.0040	0.0080	0.0120	0.0160	0.0199	0.0239	0.0279	0.0319	0.0359
0.1	0.0398	0.0438	0.0478	0.0517	0.0557	0.0596	0.0636	0.0675	0.0714	0.0754
0.2	0.0793	0.0832	0.0871	0.0910	0.0948	0.0987	0.1026	0.1064	0.1103	0.1141
0.3	0.1179	0.1217	0.1255	0.1293	0.1331	0.1368	0.1406	0.1443	0.1480	0.1517
0.4	0.1554	0.1591	0.1628	0.1664	0.1700	0.1736	0.1772	0.1808	0.1844	0.1879
0.5	0.1915	0.1950	0.1985	0.2019	0.2054	0.2088	0.2123	0.2157	0.2190	0.2224
0.6	0.2258	0.2291	0.2324	0.2357	0.2389	0.2422	0.2454	0.2486	0.2518	0.2549
0.7	0.2580	0.2612	0.2642	0.2673	0.2704	0.2734	0.2764	0.2794	0.2823	0.2852
0.8	0.2881	0.2910	0.2939	0.2967	0.2996	0.3023	0.3051	0.3078	0.3106	0.3133
0.9	0.3159	0.3186	0.3212	0.3238	0.3264	0.3289	0.3315	0.3340	0.3365	0.3389
1.0	0.3413	0.3438	0.3461	0.3485	0.3508	0.3531	0.3554	0.3577	0.3599	0.3621
1.1	0.3643	0.3665	0.3686	0.3708	0.3729	0.3749	0.3770	0.3790	0.3810	0.3830
1.2	0.3849	0.3869	0.3888	0.3907	0.3925	0.3944	0.3962	0.3980	0.3997	0.4015
1.3	0.4032	0.4049	0.4066	0.4082	0.4099	0.4115	0.4131	0.4147	0.4162	0.4177
1.4	0.4192	0.4207	0.4222	0.4236	0.4251	0.4265	0.4279	0.4292	0.4306	0.4319
1.5	0.4332	0.4345	0.4357	0.4370	0.4382	0.4394	0.4406	0.4418	0.4429	0.4441
1.6	0.4452	0.4463	0.4474	0.4484	0.4495	0.4505	0.4515	0.4525	0.4535	0.4545
1.7	0.4554	0.4564	0.4573	0.4582	0.4591	0.4599	0.4608	0.4616	0.4625	0.4633
1.8	0.4641	0.4649	0.4656	0.4664	0.4671	0.4678	0.4686	0.4693	0.4699	0.4706
1.9	0.4713	0.4719	0.4726	0.4732	0.4738	0.4744	0.4750	0.4756	0.4761	0.4767
2.0	0.4772	0.4778	0.4783	0.4788	0.4793	0.4798	0.4803	0.4808	0.4812	0.4817
2.1	0.4821	0.4826	0.4830	0.4834	0.4838	0.4842	0.4846	0.4850	0.4854	0.4857
2.2	0.4861	0.4864	0.4868	0.4871	0.4875	0.4878	0.4881	0.4884	0.4887	0.4890
2.3	0.4893	0.4896	0.4898	0.4901	0.4904	0.4906	0.4090	0.4911	0.4913	0.4916
2.4	0.4918	0.4920	0.4922	0.4925	0.4927	0.4929	0.4931	0.4932	0.4934	0.4936
2.5	0.4938	0.4940	0.4941	0.4943	0.4945	0.4946	0.4948	0.4949	0.4951	0.4952
2.6	0.4953	0.4955	0.4956	0.4957	0.4959	0.4960	0.4961	0.4962	0.4963	0.4964
2.7	0.4965	0.4966	0.4967	0.4968	0.4969	0.4970	0.4971	0.4972	0.4973	0.4974
2.8	0.4974	0.4975	0.4976	0.4977	0.4977	0.4978	0.4979	0.4979	0.4980	0.4981
2.9	0.4981	0.4982	0.4982	0.4983	0.4984	0.4984	0.4985	0.4985	0.4986	0.4986
3.0	0.4987	0.4987	0.4987	0.4988	0.4988	0.4989	0.4989	0.4989	0.4990	0.4990
3.1	0.4990	0.4991	0.4991	0.4991	0.4992	0.4992	0.4992	0.4992	0.4993	0.4993
3.2	0.4993	0.4993	0.4994	0.4994	0.4994	0.4994	0.4994	0.4995	0.4995	0.4995
3.3	0.4995	0.4995	0.4995	0.4996	0.4996	0.4996	0.4996	0.4996	0.4996	0.4997
3.4	0.4997	0.4997	0.4997	0.4997	0.4997	0.4997	0.4997	0.4997	0.4997	0.4998
3.5	0.4998	0.4998	0.4998	0.4998	0.4998	0.4998	0.4998	0.4998	0.4998	0.4998
3.6	0.4998	0.4998	0.4999	0.4999	0.4999	0.4999	0.4999	0.4999	0.4999	0.4999
3.7	0.4999	0.4999	0.4999	0.4999	0.4999	0.4999	0.4999	0.4999	0.4999	0.4999
3.8	0.4999	0.4999	0.4999	0.4999	0.4999	0.4999	0.4999	0.4999	0.4999	0.4999
3.9	0.5000	0.5000	0.5000	0.5000	0.5000	0.5000	0.5000	0.5000	0.5000	0.5000

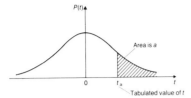

Table A.2 Percentile values (t_a) for the t-distribution. (Adapted from
Table 3 of A.C. Bajpai, I.M. Calus and J.A. Fairley, 1978
Statistical Methods for Engineers and Scientists, Wiley.)

v	a 0.1	0.05	0.025	0.01	0.005	0.001	0.0005
1	3.08	6.31	12.70	31.80	63.70	318.00	637.00
2	1.89	2.92	4.30	6.96	9.92	22.30	31.60
3	1.64	2.35	3.18	4.54	5.84	10.20	12.90
4	1.53	2.13	2.78	3.75	4.60	7.17	8.61
5	1.48	2.02	2.57	3.36	4.03	5.89	6.87
6	1.44	1.94	2.45	3.14	3.71	5.21	5.96
7	1.41	1.89	2.36	3.00	3.50	4.78	5.41
8	1.40	1.86	2.31	2.90	3.36	4.50	5.04
9	1.38	1.83	2.26	2.82	3.25	4.30	4.78
10	1.37	1.81	2.23	2.76	3.17	4.14	4.59
11	1.36	1.80	2.20	2.72	3.11	4.02	4.44
12	1.36	1.78	2.18	2.68	3.05	3.93	4.32
13	1.35	1.77	2.16	2.65	3.01	3.85	4.22
14	1.34	1.76	2.14	2.62	2.98	3.79	4.14
15	1.34	1.75	2.13	2.60	2.95	3.73	4.07
16	1.34	1.75	2.12	2.58	2.92	3.69	4.02
17	1.33	1.74	2.11	2.57	2.90	3.65	3.96
18	1.33	1.73	2.10	2.55	2.88	3.61	3.92
19	1.33	1.73	2.09	2.54	2.86	3.58	3.88
20	1.33	1.72	2.09	2.53	2.85	3.55	3.85
21	1.32	1.72	2.08	2.52	2.83	3.53	3.82
22	1.32	1.72	2.07	2.51	2.82	3.50	3.79
23	1.32	1.71	2.07	2.50	2.81	3.48	3.77
24	1.32	1.71	2.06	2.49	2.80	3.47	3.74
25	1.32	1.71	2.06	2.49	2.79	3.45	3.72
26	1.32	1.71	2.06	2.48	2.78	3.44	3.71
27	1.31	1.70	2.05	2.47	2.77	3.42	3.69
28	1.31	1.70	2.05	2.47	2.76	3.41	3.67
29	1.31	1.70	2.05	2.46	2.76	3.40	3.66
30	1.31	1.70	2.04	2.46	2.75	3.38	3.65
40	1.30	1.68	2.02	2.42	2.70	3.31	3.55
60	1.30	1.67	2.00	2.39	2.66	3.23	3.46
120	1.29	1.66	1.98	2.36	2.62	3.16	3.37
∞	1.28	1.64	1.96	2.33	2.58	3.09	3.29

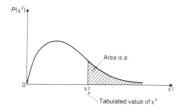

Table A.3 Percentile values (χ_a^2) for the χ^2-distribution. (Adapted from Table 5 of A.C. Bajpai, I.M. Calus and J.A. Fairley, 1978 *Statistical Methods for Engineers and Scientists*, Wiley.)

v	*a* 0.995	0.99	0.975	0.95	0.9	0.1	0.05	0.025	0.01	0.005	0.001
1	0.00	0.00	0.00	0.00	0.02	2.71	3.84	5.02	6.63	7.88	10.83
2	0.01	0.02	0.05	0.10	0.21	4.61	5.99	7.38	9.21	10.60	13.82
3	0.07	0.11	0.22	0.35	0.58	6.25	7.81	9.35	11.34	12.84	16.27
4	0.21	0.30	0.48	0.71	1.06	7.78	9.49	11.14	13.28	14.86	18.47
5	0.41	0.55	0.83	1.15	1.61	9.24	11.07	12.83	15.09	16.75	20.52
6	0.68	0.87	1.24	1.64	2.20	10.64	12.59	14.45	16.81	18.55	22.46
7	0.99	1.24	1.69	2.17	2.83	12.02	14.07	16.01	18.48	20.28	24.32
8	1.34	1.65	2.18	2.73	3.49	13.36	15.51	17.53	20.09	21.96	26.12
9	1.73	2.09	2.70	3.33	4.17	14.68	16.92	19.02	21.67	23.59	27.88
10	2.16	2.56	3.25	3.94	4.87	15.99	18.31	20.48	23.21	25.19	29.59
11	2.60	3.05	3.82	4.57	5.58	17.28	19.68	21.92	24.72	26.76	31.26
12	3.07	3.57	4.40	5.23	6.30	18.55	21.03	23.34	26.22	28.30	32.91
13	3.57	4.11	5.01	5.89	7.04	19.81	22.36	24.74	27.69	29.82	34.53
14	4.07	4.66	5.63	6.57	7.79	21.06	23.68	26.12	29.14	31.32	36.12
15	4.60	5.23	6.26	7.26	8.55	22.31	25.00	27.49	30.58	32.80	37.70
16	5.14	5.81	6.91	7.96	9.31	23.54	26.30	28.85	32.00	34.27	39.25
17	5.70	6.41	7.56	8.67	10.09	24.77	27.59	30.19	33.41	35.72	40.79
18	6.26	7.01	8.23	9.39	10.86	25.99	28.87	31.53	34.81	37.16	42.31
19	6.84	7.63	8.91	10.12	11.65	27.20	30.14	32.85	36.19	38.58	43.82
20	7.43	8.26	9.59	10.85	12.44	28.41	31.41	34.17	37.57	40.00	45.32
21	8.03	8.90	10.28	11.59	13.24	29.62	32.67	35.48	38.93	41.40	46.80
22	8.64	9.54	10.98	12.34	14.04	30.81	33.92	36.78	40.29	42.80	48.27
23	9.26	10.20	11.69	13.09	14.85	32.01	35.17	38.08	41.64	44.18	49.73
24	9.89	10.86	12.40	13.85	15.66	33.20	36.42	39.36	42.98	45.56	51.18
25	10.52	11.52	13.12	14.61	16.47	34.38	37.65	40.65	44.31	46.93	52.62
26	11.16	12.20	13.84	15.38	17.29	35.56	38.89	41.92	45.64	48.29	54.05
27	11.81	12.88	14.57	16.15	18.11	36.74	40.11	43.19	46.96	49.64	55.48
28	12.46	13.56	15.31	16.93	18.94	37.92	41.34	44.46	48.28	50.99	56.89
29	13.12	14.26	16.05	17.71	19.77	39.09	42.56	45.72	49.59	52.34	58.30
30	13.79	14.95	16.79	18.49	20.60	40.26	43.77	46.98	50.89	53.67	59.70
40	20.71	22.16	24.43	26.51	29.05	51.81	55.76	59.34	63.69	66.77	73.40
50	27.99	29.71	32.36	34.76	37.69	63.17	67.50	71.42	76.15	79.49	86.66
60	35.53	37.48	40.48	43.19	46.46	74.40	79.08	83.30	88.38	91.95	99.61
70	43.28	45.44	48.76	51.74	55.33	85.53	90.53	95.02	100.40	104.20	112.30
80	51.17	53.54	57.15	60.39	64.28	96.58	101.90	106.60	112.30	116.30	124.80
90	59.20	61.75	65.65	69.13	73.29	107.60	113.10	118.10	124.10	128.30	137.20
100	67.33	70.06	74.22	77.93	82.36	118.50	124.30	129.60	135.80	140.20	149.40

Table A.4   Critical values of the
correlation coefficient

v	α 0.05	0.01
1	0.9969	0.9999
2	0.9500	0.9900
3	0.8783	0.9587
4	0.8114	0.9172
5	0.7545	0.8745
6	0.7067	0.8343
7	0.6664	0.7977
8	0.6319	0.7646
9	0.6021	0.7348
10	0.5760	0.7079
11	0.5529	0.6835
12	0.5324	0.6614
13	0.5139	0.6411
14	0.4973	0.6226
15	0.4821	0.6055
16	0.4683	0.5897
17	0.4555	0.5751
18	0.4438	0.5614
19	0.4329	0.5487
20	0.4227	0.5368

References

The following British standards (BS), code of practice (CP) and draft for development (DD) are published by the British Standards Institution, London.

BS 410 (1976) *Specification for Test Sieves.*

BS 812 (1975) *Methods for Sampling and Testing of Mineral Aggregates, Sands and Fillers.* Part 2, *Physical properties.* Part 3, *Mechanical properties.*

BS 882 (1983) *Aggregates from Natural Sources for Concrete.*

BS 2846 (1975) *Guide to Statistical Interpretation of Data.* Part 1, *Routine Analysis of Quantitative Data.*

BS 5328 (1981) *Methods for Specifying Concrete, Including Ready-mix Concrete.*

BS 5606 (1978) *Code of Practice for Accuracy in Building.*

BS 5703 (1980) *Guide to Data Analysis and Quality Control Using Cusum Techniques.* Part 1, *Introduction to cusum charting.*

CP 110 (1972) *The Structural Use of Concrete.* Part 1, *Design, Materials and Workmanship.*

DD 22 (1972) *Recommendations for the Co-ordination of Dimensions in Building. Tolerances and Fits for Building. The Calculation of Work Sizes and Joint Clearances for Building Components.*

Index